CONSTABLE ON THE PROWL

A perfect feel-good read from one
of Britain's best-loved authors

Constable Nick Mystery Book 2

NICHOLAS RHEA

JOFFE
BOOKS

Revised edition 2020
Joffe Books, London
www.joffebooks.com

Cover credit: Colin Williamson
www.colinwilliamsonprints.com

ISBN: 978-1-78931-368-0

CHAPTER ONE

Good things of day begin to droop and drowse,
While night's black agents to their prey do rouse.
                    WILLIAM SHAKESPEARE — *Macbeth*

For the police officer, night-duty is a time to reflect upon his duties, to ponder upon the meaning of life and to assess the value of the police service as a career. Alone in the midnight hours with nothing but dead leaves, stray cats and legends of ghosts and ghoulies to accompany him, the police officer goes about his multifarious tasks unseen and unpraised. In his solitude, he deals with all manner of incidents and problems, and there is no one to thank him or console him, although if he errs in the smallest way, it can be guaranteed that someone will see him and report his misdemeanour to a higher authority.

Alternatively, the witness will write to his local newspaper about the reduction in police standards or the lack of internal discipline within the Force. This area of injustice is stoically accepted by members of the Force. Perhaps they know the writings of 'Junius' (*circa* 1770) who said, 'The injustice done to an individual is sometimes of service to the public'.

With such dangers at the back of his mind, it is fair to say that every police officer is nurtured upon a diet of nights. In police jargon, "Nights" is that period of eight agonising hours which stretch interminably from 10 pm until 6 am, or in some areas from 11 pm until 7 am. Sometimes the duty is worked a week at a stretch; on other occasions it is worked by performing two Nights, followed by two Late Turns (2 pm until 10 pm) and then three Early Turns (6 am until 2 pm). This involves "quick changeovers" when one seldom seems to sleep between those spells of bleary-eyed periods of work.

Some police forces try to ease the eternal lack of sleep by starting with Early Turn, then going on to Nights and finishing with Late Turns. Then there is the sequence Nights, Early, Late or even Late, Early, Nights or in fact any other combination, all of which are designed to ensure the maximum of work is crammed into the shortest period of time with a minimum of hours wasted in sleep.

Another attempt to baffle the policeman's sleeping routine is Half Nights. This is the period of eight hours from 6 pm until 2 am, or from 5 pm until 1 am. This duty is often welcomed during a period of full nights because it enables at least some of the night to be spent in bed and is therefore considered a perk or even a devious way of saying "thank you" for some obscure task well performed.

Many youngsters start their police career by working three weeks of full nights, broken only by a rest day or two somewhere during that tortuous spell. This first session is a long and extremely exhausting affair because sleep patterns of many normal years are interrupted, and the constable's endurance is tested by the requirement to remain awake, or at least to have the appearance of remaining awake, in spite of crushing weariness and sore feet. By the onset of Night No. 3 the policeman's sleep pattern has adjusted reasonably well to the demands placed upon it. One of these demands is the ability to eat breakfast at 2 am, followed by another at 6 am which ought, in the strictest of sequences, to be called lunch but which never is. There is little wonder that police stations reverberate with strange gastronomic sounds at such mealtimes — stomachs do need to protest from time to time.

A period of sleep follows a night-duty and this lasts until around two or three in the afternoon, which is a time free to bathe one's feet and have a nap. By nine o'clock in the evening, it is back into uniform for a rapid supper. Sandwiches are collected, and a flask is filled with hot liquid like coffee, tea or soup, then it's off to the station to parade at 9.45 pm in readiness for another period of lucernal duty.

By the time the officer has totally adjusted to his changed bodily rhythms it is time to have a day off. It is then necessary to readjust to a sort of normality, a task which is not difficult after only two or three nights, but which is nigh impossible after a long, breaking-in spell of three weeks full nights. Jetlag has nothing on this period of readjustment for it requires a total rethink on teeth-cleaning routines and toilet necessities, all aggravated by weakening torch batteries and the absence of all-night torch battery emporiums.

If this long-enforced spell of somnambulism appears to be futile, it does have a purpose. The idea is to allow the budding constable to become properly acquainted with his beat before he is turned loose upon an unsuspecting public in the full glare of British daylight. It is reasoned that in the wee small hours of the morning he can potter about the town, often accompanied by a seasoned local officer, to learn all about vulnerable properties, to discover places where cups of tea can be obtained at any hour of the night, to know which bakers use police officers to test the quality of their buns and to locate shops which offer discounts. There is the added bonus of discovering windows at which attractive ladies undress without curtains. It is also advantageous to be shown hiding places where the sergeant never looks, along with a host of other useful information. A lot of experience is gained on night-duty. It is the foundation of future "bobbying".

After the introductory term, the young officer is turned out to face his public with his training-school confidence either pleasantly consolidated or totally shattered by the experiences of those three weeks.

It is of such experiences that I now write for this book relates some incidents which have occurred during prowling periods of night-duty.

I feel that it is prudent from the outset to state that the term "night" is of considerable academic interest to the prowling police officer. It has so many different meanings within the law of England, many of which affect the performance of the bobby's duty. Although the law has dramatically changed since my early days in the Force, the definition of "night" continues to be interesting.

I first learned of the legal intricacies of 'night' at my Initial Training Centre where, by flicking through my official issue of *Moriarty's Police Law* I learned that there were several definitions of "night"; they were as follows:

Night — arrest; Night — Billiards; Night — burglary; Night — disguised with intent; Night — dogs; Night — larceny; Night-lights on vehicles; Night — loitering; Night — malicious damage; Night — offences; Night — Old Metal Dealers; Night — poaching; Night — spring guns, etc.; Night — walkers; and Night — Refreshment Houses. The problem was that the word "night" bore little resemblance to our night-duty times and indicated something different in most of the indexed cases. In addition, there were other "nights" like Night — arrest for indictable offences; Night — cafes, offences in; Night — employment; Night — work (women) and finally, as if to clarify it all, an entry entitled Night — Meaning Of.

For example, "night" for the purpose of the convention concerning the night work of women employed in industry, meant a period of at least eleven consecutive hours, including the interval between ten o'clock in the evening and five o'clock in the morning. Under the Larceny Act of 1916 then in force, but now superseded by the Theft Act of 1968, the term "night" meant the interval between 9 pm in the evening and 6 am the following day. In those days, an offence committed during the night-hours was considered infinitely more serious than a similar one committed during the day-time, consequently lots of officers patrolled the streets in case something fearsome occurred and lots of emphasis was placed upon things which might go wrong in the night. The officers had to know how to cope with anything that might arise, be it a domestic disturbance between man and wife or an aircraft crash upon the town.

Typical of the things learned was that a licensee with a billiards table must not allow anyone to use a table or instrument between 1 am and 8 am, a provision made under the Gaming Act of 1845. Another learned gem was that burglary was a crime which could be committed only between 9 pm and 6 am; if it occurred at any other time it was known as housebreaking, shop-breaking or by some other suitably descriptive name. The same period of night, 9 pm until 6 am, was also featured in the Larceny Act for many offences, including the famous Four Night Misdemeanours. These were:

1. Being found by night in any building with intent to commit felony therein;
2. Being found by night and having in his possession without lawful excuse any key, picklock, crow, jack, bit or other implement of housebreaking;
3. Being found by night armed with any dangerous weapon or instrument with intent to break into a building and commit felony therein;
4. Being found by night having his face blackened or disguised with intent to commit a felony.

For the purpose of keeping dogs under control, the period "night" meant the period between sunset and sunrise, while the laws governing lights on vehicles determined that "night" comprised the hours of darkness which were specified as the time between half-an-hour after sunset until half-an-hour before sunrise, although under a 1927 Act, it meant, during summertime, the period between one hour after sunset and one hour before sunrise in any locality. The reporting of offenders under such a multiplicity of rules could be hazardous although we were helped by a High Court case in 1899 *(Gordon* v *Caun)* which determined that sunset meant sunset according to local, not Greenwich, time.

So many references to "night" meant that all manner of juicy crimes could be committed, many of which gloried in the realm of felony. A felony was A Most Serious Matter, like *entering* a dwelling-house in the night or *breaking* into homes which was called burglary. It was felonious to lie or loiter in any highway, yard or other place during the night. Other Less Serious Matters, known as Misdemeanours, included Old Metal Dealers who were convicted of receiving stolen goods, making purchases between 6 pm and 9 am, and prostitutes or night-walkers loitering or importuning in any street.

In addition, there were those villains who set spring-traps to catch humans, although at that time, the 1950s, it was not illegal to set them between sunset and sunrise if it was done to protect one's dwelling-house. Non-licensed refreshment houses must not be kept open between 10 pm and 5 am, while pubs were subjected to a whole host of rules which we had to memorise.

With all this potential illegal activity, it follows that night-time patrols were full of interest, although it ought to be said that the interesting things were rarely related to any of these statutes. Most of them had grown seriously out of date during the first half of the 20th century and were ignored to a large degree. None the less, they did exist, and they were the law.

Having studiously learned all the necessary definitions of "night" and having calculated when one was supposed to be on duty, we were exhorted to go out and fight crime. A suitable town was selected by Headquarters, one which was deemed ideal for the operational birth of a budding bobby and it was to such places that we were dispatched. There were several suitable towns in the North Riding of Yorkshire and the one selected as my tutorial community was Strensford. To this peaceful place I was dispatched to quell riots, solve crimes, arrest burglars, catch rapists and report cyclists without lights. It was my time of learning, my period of studying police procedures and of learning the craft of bobbying from seasoned men. It was also a time to appreciate some of the dilemmas into which members of the public managed to get themselves.

No policeman ever forgets those first faltering steps of nights. If there is a time when the public is at its most vulnerable, it is during the hours of darkness, or between sunset and sunrise, or between the period half-an-hour before sunset until half-an-hour after sunrise . . .

Having been posted to Strensford, I began to learn the craft of being cunning. I began to fearlessly shake hands with doorknobs and learned how to make use of the shadows to conceal myself from everyone, including the sergeant. Hiding from the sergeant was considered good sport, particularly when it was possible to observe him seeking ourselves. Strensford taught me a lot.

I learned never to put my weight upon a doorknob when trying it for security. It could be guaranteed that that particular door was insecure and that it would pitch me headlong into the shop, to land in a tub of rotting tomatoes or a pile of ovenware or other noisome paraphernalia. The alarm created in the bedrooms of nearby slumbering members of the public can easily be imagined, so doorknobs were treated with great respect. Back doors were treated with even greater respect because they were frequently left open by shopkeepers or their staff as they rushed home at 5 pm, trusting to God and the patrolling policeman to save a lifetime's work from opportunist villains. Some doorknobs abutted the street and they were simple to cope with; others were in deep recesses where many a courting couple has disturbed a policeman going about his legitimate business. Some were along paths or alleys and others up rickety steep stairs. One could almost write a "Constable's Guide to Door Knobs" after contending with such a range.

The idea of this twice-nightly friendship ritual with doorknobs (once before the meal break and once afterwards) coupled with an examination of windows was to make sure no one had been burgled. All "property" as we termed it, must be "tried". That was our main role during the night, while the supervisory sergeant surreptitiously prowled in our wake to check that none of us omitted to discover unlocked shops or attacked premises. If we did miss a knob, we were in trouble, although it did occur to me that if the sergeant tried all the knobs in the town, why did we bother? It seemed such an elementary question that I was terrified to ask it in case the answer made me appear a naïve fool.

If we found an insecure place, we had to enter it and face the unknown foe inside. Biting our chin-straps to silence rattling teeth and in pitch darkness, we must search the place for villainous felons, or people with faces blackened by night and other evil creatures. God knows what we would have done if we'd found anyone!

Having found no one, and having noted that the exposed stock appeared untouched, we had then to make our way on foot to the office to discover the name of the key-holder. The next stage was to drag him from his bed with the news that he'd almost lost everything that was dear to him.

Some key-holders appeared to relish being knocked up at all hours because they regularly left open their shops, pubs, banks, offices or clubs. For others, however, the appearance of a cold, grim-faced constable at their door at three in the morning was enough to ensure they locked up in future. Others couldn't understand why we didn't simply drop the latch ourselves instead of making such a fuss. Such an action could be fraught with danger. If something had been stolen and its absence discovered after the policeman's visit, all sorts of accusations would be levelled at the patrolling bobby. There are plenty of unsavoury types all too eager to concoct stories too; so we checked insecure premises very thoroughly in the presence of some responsible person.

The simplest way to complete one's allocation of property each night was to ignore it entirely and curl up for a sleep in a telephone kiosk. There were officers who were very able at this; many equipped themselves with portable alarm-clocks to rouse them from their cramped slumbers, happy in the knowledge that the sergeant would make the tour and find all the insecure properties. It meant a telling off, but it saved a lot of boot leather, torch batteries and leg ache. Some dedicated constables went on night-duty armed with reels of black cotton. Having checked a property for secure doors and windows, these cotton-toting constables would fasten a length of cotton about chest or knee height across the path or doorway. Any intruder would break the strand, the logic being that the second tour of one's property would not involve extensive walking along paths and through gardens. It would comprise nothing more than shining a torch upon selected pieces of black cotton. If the cotton was broken, someone had been. The trouble was that it might have been the sergeant, it might have been legitimate visitors, or it might have been a villain. There was no way of telling, so I did not rely upon the black cotton syndrome. Besides, it was not the easiest of tasks, finding black cotton at night.

One of my tutorial sergeants at Strensford had a nasty habit of finding properties open in advance of the patrolling constable. He would then sit in them, secretly, until the arrival of the policeman. If the policeman diligently found the insecurity, praise was heaped upon his shining cap, but if he did not find it, he was in dire trouble for neglect of duty. It rapidly became obvious when Sarge was playing his game because no one saw him around the town. Sometimes, he did not turn up at the station for his mid-shift meal break, so we knew he was sitting in a shop, waiting to pounce.

If that was his contribution to crime prevention, ours was equally good. When he was in charge, we would hurry around our beats to check those properties we knew were most vulnerable or in the hands of careless owners. If we found an insecure or open door which had not been burgled or forced, we did not action it immediately. We left it alone.

Sarge would potter along to find the self-same door some time later and would disappear inside to begin his constable-catching vigil. He failed to realise that we knew he was there. We would leave him there until shortly before six o'clock in the morning when one of us would return to the premises and "find" the insecurity. Did he praise us? Not on your life; we got a bulling for being late in making the find, but he gradually got the message. After sitting alone all night among objects like sausages, ladies' knickers, fruit, pans and antiques, he decided there were better ways of passing the time.

Another valuable lesson during those early weeks in the Force was the art of concealment at night. The dark uniform lent itself to invisibility and it was easy to stand in the shadows to watch the world pass by. At night, policemen walk along the inner edges of footpaths, close to the walls in order to be unseen, while shop doorways possess excellent concealment properties, as do areas beneath trees and shrubs.

When concealed, it is necessary to pass messages to one another and in those days before we had personal radio sets, lots of unofficial messages were passed with the aid of our torches. One's colleagues would stand in the shadows and announce the pending arrival of the sergeant, inspector or superintendent, or the movements of a suspected person or indeed anything else, merely by flashing a torch. We had a code of flashes for supervisory officers — one for a superintendent which represented the solitary crown of rank upon his shoulder, two for an inspector and his pips, and three for a sergeant with his stripes. Coded messages of this kind could be passed silently over very great distances and we would sometimes take advantage of the reflections in shop windows. This allowed us to pass messages around corners.

All this could be achieved while remaining invisible. In fact, the simple act of standing still often renders a policeman invisible and I've known persons stand and talk to one another literally a couple of feet from me, totally unaware of my eaves-dropping presence. That's not possible in a panda car.

It was considered great sport to conceal oneself in a darkened doorway along the known routes of gentlemen who walked home late at night, having been on the razzle or having supped late in a friendly pub. As the pensive gent wandered slowly along his way, the amiable neighbourhood constable would step silently from the shadows immediately behind him and in a loud voice bid him 'GOODNIGHT'. This had the remarkable effect of speeding him along his journey with hairs standing erect and icicles jangling down his spine. The long-term effect was to make him change his route or abandon his lonesome trails.

Once I unwittingly scared the pants off a late reveller. It was a cold, freezing night and my feet were like blocks of ice. About two in the morning I decided to get a little relief by sitting on one of those large metal containers which house the mechanical gadgetry of traffic lights and which are invariably painted green. The containers are about four feet high and rather slender, so I hoisted myself on to the box and sat there, my large cape spreading from my shoulders and concealing the top of this convenient seat. As I perched there, hugging myself for warmth, along came a late-night reveller, singing gently to himself as he came towards me. It was clear he did not know I was there, and he almost ran into me. I said from a great height, "Goodnight."

His glazed eyes raised themselves suddenly to heaven and in a beery breath, he cried, "God Almighty, a bloody bat!" and burst into a staggering gallop. I felt sure he would be sober when he arrived home.

One indispensable accessory to the art of performing night-duty in those stirring times at Strensford was the Clock. Whether or not the system applied to every police station or whether it was unique to my first nick, I do not know. It was undoubtedly a very cunning and complicated fabrication where time was altered with the twofold intention of baffling the bobby and thwarting the thief.

The clock operated as follows. As I have already mentioned, policemen did not possess personal radio sets at that time. Having left the cosy warmth of the police office, they were effectively out of range of patrolling supervisory officers. Furthermore, if anything happened, the constable could not be contacted and dispatched to the scene of any incident. As we had no luxurious methods of communication like police boxes with direct lines to the station, we made use of public telephone kiosks.

We would stand outside selected kiosks at given times, there to await the arrival of a sergeant or a telephone call announcing that horrific things had happened and that our presence was immediately required. We had to stand outside those red-painted boxes for five minutes every half-hour of an eight-hour shift, moving from one to another in a monotonous, regulated sequence — GPO Kiosk, Fishmarket Kiosk, New Quay Kiosk, Golden Lion Kiosk, Laundry Kiosk, GPO Kiosk again . . . and so on. These five-minute waiting periods were known as "points".

The situation was that no one dare miss a point. Even if something catastrophic occurred, one must never miss a point — exciting crime inquiries were abandoned for the sake of making points, gorgeous blondes were not chatted up due to the fear of missing points, valuable clues were not examined in case we missed our points. The making of points dominated our lives.

The method of patrolling a beat was therefore along well-trodden paths between points. The town was divided into several beats, each of which had a different combination of available kiosks with points at differing times. When lots of bobbies were on duty with their points staggered around the Greenwich clock, a policeman could be contacted fairly quickly. A plethora of bobbies might, in a speeded-up film sequence, be seen to be whizzing across one another's paths but never quite making contact. It wasn't a bad system really, but it had one shocking weakness.

If a policeman was at any kiosk at exactly the same time every day then the burglars, housebreakers, robbers, rapists and other sundry rogues would get to know this. They would know the movements of the local constabulary and, having worked out their timing and movements, would perpetrate their foulest deeds while we were busy making points. That was the flaw.

The Clock was therefore designed to beat the villains — it would baffle the burglar, harry the housebreaker and rattle robbers and rapists.

The Clock itself was a circular wooden board attached to the wall of the Charge Office. It was marked with numerals taken from a police uniform and they were spaced around its outer circumference in exactly the same way as the face of a genuine clock, reading from 1 to 11, and with zero where 12 would normally be. The Clock had a solitary pointer which could be moved around the face to indicate one of the aforementioned numbers.

Thus the pointer might indicate five, ten, fifteen, twenty and so forth up to fifty-five minutes. In addition, all officers were supplied with a little book containing the dates of every month. Beside each date was a figure from the face of the Clock. Thus on 10 January the Clock might show twenty. On 26 February it might show five, and so on, for every day of the year, including leap years. It didn't really matter what it showed, so long as everyone knew and worked on the same basis, hence the explanatory book.

If the Clock showed five on a particular day it meant that all points were five minutes later than scheduled. Thus a 12 noon point shown at the GPO Kiosk would be made at 12.05 pm. If the Clock showed fifty-five, the point would be made at 12.55 pm, fifty-five minutes late.

When beginning a tour of duty, therefore, it was vital to check the Clock and to make a note of its reading in one's notebook. The sergeant would then allocate us to our beats and off we'd go. This meant an entry in one's notebook and in one's memory bank that one was working No 6 Beat with points normally at quarter to and quarter past the hour, but with today's Clock at fifty-five.

Sometimes beats were worked in reverse. The Clock could also be given a minus quality. Working a beat backwards with the Clock on minus ten was a hilarious affair especially when everyone else was working his beat in the normal sequence with the Clock on plus five.

If the system was designed to baffle the burglar, it did not succeed because the burglar never got the chance to study the sequence of our beats anyway. They were never fully manned.

In the Clock's favour, it certainly confounded the unfortunate office-bound constables who spent their time ringing telephone kiosks in the hope that someone might answer. There were times when the whole town was alive with the sound of bells and many a worker has risen early thinking his alarm was sounding. And many a citizen has answered the telephone to find a puzzled policeman at the other end asking if he, the citizen, could see a policeman nearby. Policemen are never around when they're wanted.

In fact, it was probably this system which gave rise to that popular legend when, in truth, the policemen couldn't find a policeman when they wanted one.

It was with such a wealth of experience in the art of working nights that I was posted to Aidensfield which was considered a progressive station because it did not operate the Clock.

My arrival in this lovely village coincided with that period of change between the old and the new so far as village bobbies were concerned. The old idea had been to place the bobby on a rural beat and let him work the patch at his own discretion. He was never off duty and no one bothered whether or not he worked a straight eight-hour shift. He did his job as he saw fit; if he fancied digging the garden one afternoon then that was fine so long as he coped with any incident that arose.

I came to Aidensfield at the end of that casual but effective era, for the new idea was that even country bobbies should patrol for an eight-hour day on set routes.

If anything cropped up after those eight hours or before they began, the duty of attending to it would be passed to another officer who was patrolling the district. That's if he could be found . . .

The result was that, along with my colleagues, I had to work night-duty shifts in a rural area. This was not a very frequent occurrence, certainly not as often as one week in three, the system to which I had become accustomed at Strensford. On average, it worked out that I patrolled a full week of nights once in every seventeen weeks during my term at Aidensfield. One advantage was that instead of using the motorcycle, I was allowed the luxury of a motorcar in which to patrol. It had no heater and no radio, but it did have a roof and a windscreen. It was an ancient Ford of doubtful reliability and it had a well-tested tendency to proceed in a straight line at bends in the road, especially when the driver was asleep.

I wasn't sure whether I would enjoy night-duty on this large rural patch, but one fact was certain — there was no way of avoiding it.

CHAPTER TWO

Humour is odd, grotesque and wild,
Only by affection spoil'd.
JONATHAN SWIFT — To Mr Delany,
10 October 1718

On a late autumn night I left Mary and the infants in bed, locked the door of my hilltop police house and drove my motorcycle four miles into the sleepy market town of Ashfordly. This quiet place housed my Section Office and as I coasted the final ten yards into the garage to avoid waking nearby children, I noticed the tall, ramrod figure of Oscar Blaketon waiting outside. He was unsmiling and at his most severe.

I parked my machine in the garage and made sure it would not tumble over before lifting my sandwiches and flask from one of the panniers and my peaked cap and torch from the other. Thus equipped, I walked along the side of the police station and entered the tiny office. Blaketon was already inside waiting for me.

"You're late, Rhea! Ten o'clock start, you know. Not quarter past," and his fingers tapped the counter to emphasise his words.

"I booked on at ten, Sergeant, at Aidensfield. It's taken me ten minutes to get here. I was on duty during those ten minutes . . ."

"Clever sod, eh? Look son, when I was a lad, policemen began their shifts ten minutes *before* the starting-time, not ten minutes after."

"I did a few minutes in my own office, Sergeant, before I set off . . ."

"Ten o'clock start means ten o'clock. Here. Not at home. Right?"

"Yes, Sergeant." It was impossible to argue when he was in this mood.

Having diplomatically settled that point, he went on to inform me of my responsibilities over the next eight hours, not forgetting to remind me of that disputed fifteen minutes. It transpired that I had to patrol the district in the official car and was expected to make points on the hour, every hour, at nominated telephone kiosks. I had to take my meal break at Eltering Police Station, the local Sub-Divisional Office, a key to which was on the car keyring. That being the halfway stage. I must then make the return journey via the same kiosks. It seemed simple enough. My eleven o'clock point would be at Thackerston Kiosk, my midnight one at Waindale and my one o'clock at Whemmelby. During the period 1.45 am until 2.30 pm, I would be in Eltering Police Station enjoying a meat sandwich and a cup of coffee from my flask. After that I had to return via Whemmelby at three, Waindale at four and Thackerston at five. I would book off duty at Ashfordly at six and travel home, bleary-eyed, cold and undoubtedly hungry, to knock off at 6.15 am.

"There's a book of unoccupied property," he shoved a huge leather-bound volume across the counter. "Check 'em all. Houses, golf clubs, shops — the lot. Poachers'll be abroad, I reckon, and late-night boozers. Don't go to sleep in that car — it runs off the road if you do. There'll be a supervisory rank on duty in Malton — a sergeant or possibly an inspector — and he might pop out to meet you somewhere. So be there.

Also, the Malton rural night patrol will be doing the southern end of the patch — you might meet him at Eltering. The lads usually meet there for a chat — nothing wrong in that so long as you don't exceed your three-quarters of an hour meal break. Don't abuse the trust I place in you, Rhea."

"There's no radio in the car," I said inanely, wondering what the procedure was if the car broke down in a remote area, or if I needed assistance of any sort.

"True," he said, turning into his office. "True, there is no radio in the car."

Realising that my statement of the obvious would excite no further comment from Oscar, I turned my attention to the Occurrence Book. It revealed nothing of immediate interest, save a stolen car which had already been found abandoned in Scarborough. I noted some unoccupied premises from the leather-bound volume and, anxious to be off, I lifted the car keys from their hook. I checked that the office fire was stoked up sufficiently to remain burning until my return and said, "I'm off, Sergeant."

There was no reply.

I dropped the latch as I made my exit, making sure I had my door key to re-enter at six. In the garage the little Ford Anglia awaited me. I unlocked the driver's door and climbed in. It was a very basic car with no trimmings, the only interior extra being the official logbook which had to be completed after every journey. Every purchase of oil or petrol had to be entered and I checked the book to ensure that my predecessor, whoever he was, had complied with that instruction.

Happily, the log was up to date. Before venturing out I remembered another essential check, a visual examination of the exterior. This was done to check whether the vehicle had suffered any damage that might be blamed on me.

During that era policemen seldom drove cars regularly on duty. That was considered a privilege rather than a right and the exceptions were the *crème de la crème* who had been selected for motor patrol duty. It was considered a luxury to have the use of a mechanically-propelled conveyance, owned and paid for by the ratepayers. If any of us accidentally marked an official car by reversing into a gatepost or scratching it in any way we were grounded for ever. The result was that policemen who damaged cars never admitted it. The cunning offenders parked in garages or tight corners so that an unsuspecting driver would take out the vehicle without noticing the blemish. Once you were driving, the vehicle was your responsibility, which meant that any scratches, dents, bumps or bruises were deemed to have occurred through your carelessness. No arguments or excuses were entertained. It was even pointless arguing that the car had been damaged in your absence — it was your fault for leaving it in such a vulnerable position. Every driver therefore carefully checked every nut, bolt, screw, indicator light, panel, glass etc, before turning a wheel.

Various intellectual giants within the Force considered it wise to bump the night-duty car on the grounds they'd be forbidden to drive for eternity and thus unable to perform night-duty. Even greater intellectual giants felt this was not a wise move because they would have to patrol at night either on foot, on cycle or on motorcycles. The point was well taken. Apart from the chilliness of the latter possibility, motorcycle patrols in rural areas at night were guaranteed to make dogs bark, hens cackle, residents to arouse early and poachers to learn of our whereabouts. Being conscientious individuals we were careful with official vehicles.

Primitive though it was, the car was pleasant and undamaged, so I started the well-tuned engine and began to drive from the garage. Suddenly Sergeant Blaketon was right in my path and flagging me down with his torch. I stopped, wound down the window and asked, "Is there a message, Sergeant?"

"There is," he said.

I sat in silence to await the words he wished to impart, but he merely stood by the car, immobile and severe. It dawned on me that he wanted me to get out, which I did.

"Oil, water, tyres, lights, indicators," he said woodenly. "Elementary. Always check them. Always. Before every journey. It's laid down in orders. You didn't."

I didn't argue. I knew he always checked such things. He would stride around the car, looking at the aforementioned points before moving off. He performed this ritual every time, so I now did the same. Up went the bonnet and I found the oil and water levels to be fine. Indicators working, tyres at correct pressures . . .

"Goodnight, Rhea," he said, turning on his heel and vanishing into the office. I drove off, thinking about him. I remembered watching him reverse the little car from the police station drive a few weeks earlier to allow a visiting inspector to remove his car. Oscar Blaketon had got out of the Ford, performed a fleeting moment's traffic duty on the street to guide out the inspector, and then, before driving the police car back into the garage, he had performed his ritual of checking oil, water, tyres, lights and indicators. Such was his devotion to the rule-book, even though his ten-yard journey had been broken by only half a minute.

With this salutary lesson in my mind, I began my first tour of rural night-duty as Aidensfield's local bobby. The district around Aidensfield is a land of small communities, many of which boast a single shop-cum-post office, their sole business premises. Even these, however modest, must be examined by night patrols and it was a simple process to patrol in the car between the villages and to check their sparse premises before sallying to the next stop. Until 10.30 each night there was the additional task of checking the public houses, but once the night life of the area ended at 11, the world was mine.

Over the next few days a routine developed. I would arrive at Ashfordly at quarter to ten and check the car noisily so that Oscar Blaketon satisfied himself that the task was done. I would then sally forth into the unknown, making my expedition around the telephone kiosks and checking vulnerable properties in between times. One curious fact that emerged was that in every village there was a light burning, no matter what the time of night I passed through. I knew there was always someone about, someone awake in addition to myself. It meant the patrolling policeman is never totally alone and this is a reassuring fact, although it does mean that we have to be careful when we water our horses or enjoy a quick nap in the car.

One continuing problem at night was keeping awake. Even though the car did not possess a heater, warm air blew in from the engine and this had the effect of making even the most alert of occupants drop off to sleep. The solution was to open a window or park up and take a walk. Unfortunately, this remedy often came too late and the little car has frequently terminated its journey in a field or ditch, happily without serious damage. One can appreciate that, after a full week of nights, the chief purpose of the patrolling policeman is to remain awake; it is even possible to fall asleep while standing outside a telephone kiosk. When excessively tired, night-duty becomes very, very tedious.

The most welcome place during those tedious patrols was the police office at Eltering. It had a coal fire which burned all day and all night in a well-worn, but tidy room and this produced a very homely atmosphere. The chairs were antiques, being old and wooden in the Windsor style, and there was a clean but worn rug before the fire. To spend three-quarters of an hour here during a meal break on nights was extremely pleasant, if only because it offered companionship for a short time.

My colleagues who patrolled the rest of the Sub-Division also used this office for their meal breaks and quite frequently the night car from Scarborough, a fast, sleek black patrol car with a crew of two, would call in for a chat and a meal. It was customary for everyone to meet there at the same time and even the duty sergeant would come to join the chatter, laughter, card school or whatever amusement was currently popular. There could be a domino school, for example, or even a Monopoly contest.

It didn't take long to become acquainted with the men who shared this cosy spot on night-duty. The most fascinating was a huge, grizzle-haired constable whose name was

Alf Ventress. He hailed from Malton and his night-shifts came around approximately the same as mine. This meant we often met in Eltering Police Station over our meals. He was far more experienced than I, for he must have completed more than twenty-five unglamorous years in the job. A typically dour Yorkshireman, he rarely spoke to anyone while eating, but sat in the same chair each time to munch his packed meal. His chief mission was to consume his bait and drink his coffee without interruption.

His uneventful career had not given him reason to be polite or smart, and his uniform was never tidy. It always needed pressing, his boots were forever in need of a polish, while his shoulders and upper tunic were constantly covered with a combination of dandruff and cigarette ash. He chain smoked when he was not eating and the other lads tended to leave him alone. It was not policy to interrupt him because he had something of a reputation for being short-tempered. No one had actually seen him angry, but it was the way he looked at troublemakers through heavy eyebrows — it made them shrivel with anticipation of a display of anger, yet he never erupted.

For all these reasons he was nicknamed Vesuvius, the name arising from the fact that he was always covered in ash and likely to erupt at any time.

I soon learned he disliked a crowd and, if we were alone, he was good company, reminiscing and telling me yarns about his younger days in the Force. When the Scarborough motor patrol crew arrived, however, the office became alive with their chatter as they recounted hair-raising stories of their exploits and exciting dramas in which they had been involved. Their experiences made us foot patrol lads look very mundane.

Vesuvius listened but never tried to compete with them and, over the months, we all became familiar with his routine for eating his meal. His wife, whose name we never knew, always packed a cheese sandwich, two hard-boiled eggs, a piece of fruit cake and a bar of chocolate. His diet on nights never changed and he swilled it all down with a flask of steaming, dark coffee.

I can see him now. He would stride into the office, huge and menacing, as if daring anyone to occupy his fireside chair. Having settled his bulk into the seat he would stretch his legs until his feet rested on the hearth and would then open his bait tin. Out would come a clean white serviette which he spread across his lap and he would position his tin on the floor at his side. The flask of coffee stood like a sentinel beside it.

First out were the two hard-boiled eggs. He always held them aloft, one in each hand, and brought them together in front of him with a loud crack. This is known as egg jarping in the North Riding, and the action forms a type of game in some areas. This sharp action broke the shells, whereupon he peeled them and dropped the waste on to the serviette in his lap. He would then consume both eggs very rapidly before tackling the cheese sandwich. His noisy enjoyment was a treat to observe.

One night I was first into the office and within two minutes the two motor patrol lads entered. They were called Ben and Ron.

"Vesuvius in yet?" Ben asked.

"No", I said, "but he's due at any time."

He had obviously been in earlier because his bait tin stood on the counter, and so Ron lifted the lid as Ben took two eggs from his own pocket. He exchanged them with those from the bait tin, concealing Vesuvius' eggs in his coat pocket. He closed the lid and waited. Nothing more was said or done.

Five minutes later the big man entered. Without a word he sat down, lifted his bait tin from its resting-place, stretched out those huge legs towards the hearth and smiled. I watched, wondering what was going to happen next. Ben and Ron sat opposite with long, straight faces, talking earnestly about football.

Vesuvius sat back in his chair and covered his lap with the white serviette, licking his lips with anticipation.

I watched him take two eggs from his tin. I was unable to turn my eyes from them as he smiled fleetingly, licked his lips again and opened his arms wide with an egg clutched in each fist. He brought them together smartly as he always did.

They were fresh eggs. There was a sickening, sploshing noise as Vesuvius was suddenly smothered in bright yellow egg yolk and streamers of uncooked egg white. His hands were dripping while pieces of smashed shell clung to his face and hair.

He roared, "That bloody woman!" and stormed out to wash himself.

Ben and Ron burst into fits of laughter and I joined in their fun for it seemed the prank had been played upon Vesuvius many times in the past. On each occasion he blamed his wife for failing to hard-boil his eggs and we often wondered what was said to her upon his return home at six.

As my visits to Eltering grew in number I realised that poor Vesuvius was the butt of many jokes, both in the office and out of doors. I think all were designed to goad him into a display of temper, but all failed. Vesuvius never erupted. I never played jokes on him — deep down I felt sorry for this man who, in truth, had a heart of gold and a gentle word for the most deprived and depraved members of society. His bluff exterior was not a true indication of his gentle nature and he genuinely loved other people.

It was his attitude to others that led him to organise bus outings for old-age pensioners from Malton. Vesuvius would commission a coach to take a load of old folks for a day at Scarborough, or to a theatre or zoo. He'd arrange to visit establishments like York Minster, Ampleforth College, Castle Howard, Thompsons Woodcarvers of Kilburn and other places of local interest.

His kindness led to another prank at his expense. We were in Eltering police office one night when the terrible traffic twins entered. Ben and Ron were happy and laughing as usual as they settled down for their mid-morning break. As Vesuvius entered to perform his egg-breaking ritual without mishap, Ben went into the sergeant's office next door. I heard him lift the telephone and dial an extension number; then our office telephone rang. Vesuvius answered it.

"Eltering Police", he growled in his deep voice.

And I heard Ben's voice coming from the next office saying, "This is the Ryedale Coach Touring Company."

"It must be urgent to ring at this time of day," Vesuvius commented. "It's two in the morning."

And Ben replied, "It is very urgent, Mr Ventress, very urgent indeed. We've been up all night, working on revised arrangements. I'm ringing about that trip you've organised tomorrow night, to the brewery. We've had to cancel it."

"Cancel it?" bellowed Vesuvius. "Why? It's all laid on, supper an' all, for the lads. Forty lads going . . ."

"That's why I'm ringing you now, so you can cancel things. You didn't apply for a licence, you see," said Ben from the next office. Ron and myself sat enthralled, listening to both sides of this curious conversation. Vesuvius, of course, could only hear the voice on his telephone.

"Licence?" he snarled.

"Licence," said Ben solemnly. "You need a Customs and Excise licence to run bus-trips. It's a new law. It was introduced in the last budget and we forgot to tell you. It means your trip's illegal, Mr Ventress. We've no option, I'm afraid. It'll have to be cancelled. That's why I'm ringing late, before tomorrow, so you can do the necessary. Sorry."

"Can't I get a licence, then?" he asked, a picture of misery.

"Not in time for this one, but pop into the post office and ask for a Coach Outing Arrangers Licence application form. It costs £10 for a year and means you can organise trips by coach anywhere in England, except the Isle of Man and the Channel Isles. That's extra."

"I'll have to contact everybody that's booked and return their money."

"Sorry, Mr Ventress, but we daren't cooperate with an illegally run bus-trip."

"Aye, all right," and the big, unhappy man put down the receiver.

"What's up, Alf?" asked Ron, a picture of innocence.

"Bus company," he said. "I've got to cancel my trip tomorrow night. It's a pity. It's a pensioners' outing — the women-folk are all off to a bingo session, so I fixed up a trip for their husbands. We're off to a brewery at Hartlepool. Seems I need a licence to run bus-trips now. Can't get one in time

"Aw, Alf, what a shame!" Ben had reappeared and was having difficulty preventing himself bursting into laughter.

I didn't know what to do. I do appreciate a good joke, but I don't like to see people hurt and this had clearly upset poor old Vesuvius. He produced one of his pungent cigarettes and lit it, casting clouds of foul smoke about the room as he ate his cheese sandwich in silence. I didn't find it easy to be a party to this and tried to make intelligent conversation by talking shop with Ben and Ron. Finally, the terrible twins decided to leave the office, chuckling to themselves as they went.

This left me with a great problem. Should I tell him it was all a joke?

"Tell me about the bus-trip," I began. Gently, this untidy giant of a man explained how he felt sorry for pensioners without cars and without the funds and ability to get themselves around the countryside or attend functions like concerts, pantomimes and shows. He therefore arranged outings for them. He chatted on and on about some of the more enjoyable occasions and I forgot about the time. I found him a fascinating mixture of personalities. He was a stolid, gentle Yorkshire giant with a heart of gold and a softness beneath which was totally concealed by his external appearance. He looked like a perpetually angry man, yet I don't think he had an ounce of anger in him. I decided I liked Vesuvius.

My dilemma was solved before I left because the telephone rang again. It jerked me back to reality and reminded me that I had lots of property to check before my next point. As Vesuvius answered it, I got up to rinse out my flask.

Seconds later, he was smiling all over.

"The bus company again," he told me. "That chap's rung me on his way home, from a kiosk. He's just remembered — I applied before the financial year's end, before Budget Day, so I can run trips without a licence that I'd got booked up before April 4th. It's all right, Nick, and in compensation, they're giving me the best bus, the one with the television in."

"I'm pleased," I said, leaving him to his new-found happiness.

In the weeks that followed, my talks with local bobbies told me that poor old Vesuvius had been the butt of countless pranks over the years, but not one had caused him to lose his temper, nor had he retaliated violently.

There were the occasional hints of anger, like the outbursts against his wife during his egg-breaking routines, and I began to wonder if he really did have a temper. What *would* make him rise to the bait, I wondered?

I collected quite a repertoire of jokes that had been perpetrated upon him. Ben and Ron had once put Vesuvius' private car number on the Stolen Vehicles Register, with the result that he got stopped and questioned by a police patrol in Sunderland while heading north for a fishing holiday. No amount of explanation would convince the Sunderland police that it was his own vehicle until Vesuvius, in his patient way, managed to convince a sergeant that he was an honest policeman from Yorkshire. On another occasion, someone substituted the Superintendent's home telephone number for the "Dial a Story" service offered by Hull Telephone Company. It had to be poor old Vesuvius, alone in the office one night, who decided he'd like to listen to a short story, and dialled the number concerned. The Superintendent was not very pleased to be roused by the familiar tones of Vesuvius at 2.30 in the morning, and he refused to accept that the joke was not originated by PC Ventress.

If Vesuvius and his placid nature were the butt of policemen's jokes, they were also a fine target for civilian pranks.

I learned he had once arrested a local scrap merchant for stealing lengths of copper piping, and the Scrappy eventually appeared at court to be heavily fined by the magistrates.

Thereafter, he considered Vesuvius his sworn enemy. Even though the Scrappy was later arrested by other policemen and fined even more heavily from time to time, he continued to hate Vesuvius, seemingly because that had been his first arrest and therefore the start of his criminal career.

Vesuvius bore the rancour with his traditional calm until the Scrappy realised that, once every few weeks, poor old Vesuvius worked a full tour of night-duty. This meant he slept between 7 am and lunchtime, spending the early part of the day in pleasant slumbers. Vesuvius lived in his own small, neat terrace house in a quiet part of Malton, so the virulent Scrappy decided to visit that street while Vesuvius slept. He chose to park his horse-and-cart outside Vesuvius' peaceful home and announce his presence by blowing a trumpet.

The notion behind this scheme was that the trumpet would become a trademark and it would announce his whereabouts to those who wished to off-load their rubbish. They could run out of their homes and deposit it upon the waiting cart in exchange for a small payment, a *very* small payment as a rule.

To thwart retaliatory action by Vesuvius, the Scrappy changed his timing and his day. Some mornings, he would arrive at nine o'clock, others at 11 or 10.30, the result being that poor old Vesuvius never had any idea of the impending arrival of the noisy man and his blasted trumpet. He lost many hours of precious sleep because of this, but he never complained either officially or unofficially.

I learned from my colleagues at Malton that the trumpet was the pride and joy of that offending Scrappy. It was very old and very valuable, and furthermore had a deep sentimental meaning in the family, having been passed down from his great-grandfather, who had played it in a local brass band. When played properly its tone was excellent, but the puffing and blowing of this man did little to enhance its reputation. It merely produced a fearful din at his lips.

Malton police did receive complaints from other members of the public and attempts were made to confiscate the trumpet. Somehow, he managed to avoid all patrolling officers and we lacked the necessary hard evidence for a court appearance.

It was dear old Vesuvius who finally put a stop to the noise.

It happened one morning. Vesuvius had finished night-duty early and had taken four hours off duty in lieu of overtime worked. This meant he had finished work at two o'clock. By ten o'clock that same morning he was wide awake and in fact was downstairs tucking into a hefty plateful of eggs and bacon. It was at that time that the Scrappy chose to play the "Donkey Serenade" right outside Vesuvius' front door, pointing the mouth of the trumpet high at the window above. The poor fellow was carried away by the thrill of his own music, and the notes were long and loud as the unseen donkey was duly serenaded.

On hearing this foul din, Vesuvius opened his front door and was outside before the Scrappy realised what was happening. One massive fist seized the offending instrument and the other clutched the collar of the ghastly musician. Without a word Vesuvius hauled both offenders through his house and into the backyard where he released his grip of the bewildered scrap merchant.

Then, without saying a word, Vesuvius opened the door of a small brick building and, smiling at the unhappy witness, removed the mouthpiece of the trumpet. He handed this to its owner with a smile on his face then stepped inside the shed.

Inside stood a huge mangle with ancient wooden rollers, worn hollow in the centre by years of wringing out the washing of generations. Smiling quietly at the waiting man Vesuvius inserted the slender tube of the mouth end of the trumpet between the rollers and began to turn the handle.

I am assured that cries of deep anguish echoed from the horrified scrap merchant as his precious trumpet was drawn into the mangle. He was kept at arm's length by

Vesuvius who used his powerful free arm to turn the handle. Eventually, the trumpet appeared from the other side, flattened like a pancake. Vesuvius took it in his hands, seized the dirty collar again and propelled the hapless character outside. Not a word was spoken by Vesuvius as he led the Scrappy to his horse, tossed the trumpet among the other scrap on the cart, and closed his door on that episode.

The slumbering Vesuvius was never again aroused by trumpet blasts.

My respect for Vesuvius grew as I saw more of him. Due to our shift system we frequently worked nights together and those mid-shift meal breaks were regularly provided with entertainment by those terrible traffic twins, Ben and Ron. Their pranks upon Vesuvius seemed endless, although it must be said they were all harmless. Vesuvius, on his part, took them stoically and never grumbled or lost his temper. His nickname seemed all the more apt because the violent eruptions of Mount Vesuvius were not very frequent, although it did grumble and threaten from time to time. They were very similar, he and his volcano.

It was nice to get him talking. On those occasions when the traffic lads did not arrive, Vesuvius and I would chat quite amiably. He would tell me of his early service in the Force when discipline was strict, and money was poor, but he was proud to remember the days when the public respect for the bobby was at its height, and when they appreciated the work done on their behalf. A few smartly clipped ears were infinitely better than either court appearances, the advice of social workers or the utterances of bureaucrats who had no idea of how to deal with people, but who were wizards with statistics. Modern law-makers were thinkers not doers, Vesuvius would say, but he continued to act in his own way, apparently totally content with life.

He told me the modern version of the Good Samaritan parable one night, relating how a social worker had found a poor man in the ditch. The man had been violently attacked and robbed by a gang of thugs. As the injured man lay bleeding in the street the social worker said, "What an awful thing to happen. Tell me who did this to you, so that I might find him and minister to him".

As we grew to understand each other. I realised that Vesuvius was highly intelligent. He was far from the slow and dim-witted person he pretended to be and several little clues led me to this belief. The regular egg-smashing joke was one example of this. From snippets told me when we were alone he knew that Ben and Ron swapped the eggs, although he never allowed them to realise he knew of their pranks.

Whenever he was caught by their tomfoolery, he contin-ued to blame his wife for forgetting to hard-boil the eggs, but he craftily told everyone else of his knowledge. The result was that only the terrible twins were fooled by this and although it meant an egg-spattered tunic from time to time, the real fools of the incidents were Ben and Ron. Everyone else was secretly laughing at them and their ignorance. It was this attitude that gave me an insight into the complex character of the stolid, unflappable PC Ventress.

He once told me he was waiting for the right moment to return their jokes; he would wait for months if necessary. When that opportunity did arise, it was marvellous, and I was delighted to be present at their comeuppance.

I was in the office at Eltering Police Station, enjoying one of those midnight breakfasts around two o'clock in the morning. It was a summer's night, albeit cool and fresh and the moon shone brightly. Inside, Vesuvius was in his favour-ite chair, eating his usual pair of hard-boiled eggs with his napkin across his knees. Conversation was non-existent for he ate in silence, and then the terrible twins entered. There was enough slamming of doors and noise for an army of men as they breezed into the office.

"Grand night, Vesuvius," smiled Ron, unbuttoning his tunic as he settled in the chair opposite.

"Aye," agreed Vesuvius, munching his cheese sandwich.

Ben, meanwhile, had gone straight into the toilet. We heard the distinct crash of its door as he rushed inside, followed by the equally distinctive five minutes' silence. Eventually, we heard the flush of the chain and the reopening of the door, followed by a somewhat anxious reappearance of Ben.

"The keys!" he cried as he entered the office. "The bloody car keys!"

"Keys?" puzzled Ron.

"Yeh, I stuck them in my trousers pocket, like I always do. They must have lodged on the top, on my truncheon strap," and he indicated the right-hand trousers pocket. The top of his truncheon was showing, and its leather strap hung down the outside of his leg. Truncheons have a specifically made long pocket which runs down the inside of the right leg, to the knee, the entrance to which is adjacent to the usual pocket. It was not uncommon for objects to find their way into the wrong pocket, nor was it unusual for objects to get caught on the truncheon when it was in position.

"What's happened?" I asked.

"Well, there I was, sitting on the bog. I got up, my trousers still around my ankles and reached up to pull the chain. And as I stretched up, the car keys fell into the bowl — right down. They fell in at the precise moment I pulled the chain! I was too late to stop pulling — I saw the bloody things fall in but couldn't stop the flushing."

"They've gone?" gasped Ron.

"Gone," repeated Ben. "I couldn't help it, honest. What can we do?"

"Search me!"

"The inspector will play holy hell! He'll probably book us for loss or damage to county property, carelessness, dereliction of duty or some other trumped-up charge!"

"Don't you carry spares?" I asked.

"We should," Ron admitted, "but it's the second time that idiot has lost ours. He lost the other set down a drain when he got out to deal with a road accident. Tonight's keys *were* the spare set."

"Are you sure they've gone right down?" I asked, trying to be helpful.

"Sure," said Ben, sitting in a chair and removing his bait tin from his bag. "They've gone. I've checked."

Ron and I went to examine the toilet basin and it was totally empty. There was no sign of the missing keys. We searched the floor and the route back to the office, then out to the car and finally we made Ben turn out his pockets. Nothing. No car keys.

"They went down, I saw them," he repeated for the hundredth time. "I saw them fall in just as I flushed."

"I can get them back," said Vesuvius quietly, having concluded his meal. He wiped his mouth and replaced the folded serviette in its tin.

"You can?" they chorused, sitting bolt upright with relief evident on their faces.

"Dead easy," he said, wiping his mouth with the back of his hand.

"Come on, Alf," cried Ron. "Give! Put us out of our misery!"

"You know that manhole cover in the middle of the street outside, just in front of the door to the station?"

Ben nodded. It always rattled when a car drove across it and was a good warning that someone was approaching, like the Superintendent.

"Well," said Vesuvius slowly, "the channels from our station toilets go through there. I've been down before, clearing channels, years ago. That manhole is about eight feet deep and several channels pass through the bottom of it. All you have to do is climb down inside — there's steps built into the wall — and I could flush the chain until the keys are washed through. You'd get 'em back down there. Dead simple."

Ben's eyes brightened.

"You sure, Vesuvius?" he looked at me and then at Ron.

"I've done it before," said Vesuvius, standing up.

"Right," said Ben. "Let's try it. You show us."

We trooped outside, and I carried the torch. Vesuvius took the poker from the fireplace and the four of us stood

33

around the large, metal cover. Vesuvius prised up one end with the poker and we lifted it clear, placing it on the centre of the road. Somewhere, a clock struck 2.15. The town was at peace.

"Torch," someone called, and I shone the light deep inside. It was a square-shaped well, clinically clean and lined with white-tiled bricks. A metal ladder was built into one wall and the bottom would be a good eight feet or even more below us. We could see the five channels entering the base from different angles, merging into one large exit channel. It was large enough for at least one man to climb inside; at a squeeze, two could make it.

"The one on the left, nearest the exit route," Vesuvius indicated to Ron. "That's ours. If we flush our chain, the muck comes flooding down there and it's carried along that other single channel, out of sight. If Ben gets down there, he can catch it as it comes past and get your keys. The tag will help them swim along to this point."

Ben did not like the idea at all. His face told us that. For him, the entire scheme was distasteful.

"Ron, it's got to be done," said Ben. "You lost the bloody things down the hole."

"Have we any Wellingtons?" he asked. "I could stop the flow with my foot, eh? Stick my foot in that groove to halt things as they come through?"

"No Wellingtons here, Ben," said Vesuvius. "You could use your bare feet, eh? I've seen council workmen do that. Take your shoes and socks off, roll your trousers up to the knees and stick your foot in that groove. Your toes will catch the keys, eh? And you'll let the other rubbish float past."

Ben looked down at his shoes. They were black leather, nicely polished, and he did not intend wasting them. Besides, feet could be washed.

"All right," he sighed. "There's no choice. I'll do it." Standing at the edge of the hole, Ben removed his socks and shoes, rolled up his trousers to the knees and prepared to climb down the cold, damp metal stairs. They would take him to the brown earthenware floor of the manhole with its array of tiny tunnels.

"When I get down," he said, "I'll shout when I'm ready. I'll stick my foot in that channel — are you sure it's the right one, Vesuvius?"

"Aye," he said. "I'm sure. The one on the left, like I said. Stick your foot in it, toes pointing towards our building. When you're ready, give us a shout and I'll pull. I'll keep pulling the chain until your keys are washed through. It'll take a few flushes, I reckon, it's a bit of a distance."

Ron stood at the top of the hole, looking down upon his pal as he clambered nervously down the ladder. The rusty rungs hurt his feet, but soon he was on the cool, smooth floor.

"This one?" he stuck a toe into the narrow groove, as if testing the sea for the temperature of the water. Vesuvius said, "Aye," and Ben therefore planted his bare foot firmly into the channel, effectively blocking it. His toes faced the police station, as suggested.

"Right, I'm off," said Vesuvius and he went into the police station, asking me to liaise with him. I had to dart backwards and forwards making sure both parties were ready before the first pull of the chain. The distance between the toilet basin and the foot of that manhole would be some thirty yards or so, and I wondered how much effluent would have to be dislodged before the bit carrying the keys arrived at Ben's big toe.

I called to Ben. "Ready?"

"I'm ready," he replied, his face white as he peered up at me.

I rushed inside to Vesuvius.

"He's ready when you are," I announced.

"Get yourself back to that hole," he laughed. "I'll give you ten seconds. You'll enjoy this!"

Puzzled by his final remark I hurried to the vantage point on the rim and looked down.

"Count ten," I said to Ben, for want of something more appropriate.

Surprisingly, Ben did.

I heard him counting — one, two, three, four, five . . . all the time staring at his white foot bathed in the light of my torch.

"Nine, ten," he concluded.

Then I heard the sound of a heaving chain and the gurgle of an emptying cistern. Somewhere in Ben's deep chamber I heard the whooshing of an oncoming flow of water, and I heard Vesuvius shout. "First lot coming."

"First lot coming," I repeated for Ben's benefit.

Then I realised Vesuvius' ruse.

The pipe from the police station toilets did not emerge at the base of the manhole — it emerged near the top! It was about six feet above the base, dropping its discharges from a great height. It was the oncoming rush of water that warned me — the sound came from a series of pipes which entered the chamber at varying heights. I could see them now, a series of dark holes. And Ben was standing on the floor.

Too late he realised what was about to happen.

With a sighing, almost obscene noise the mess spluttered and rushed from the darkness just above Ben's head and, in seconds, he was smothered from head to toe. I heard him cough and gasp as Ron burst into fits of laughter at the sight of his poor companion whose uniform, face and hair were plastered with the foulest mess imaginable. He tried to climb out, but another whooshing noise was sounding. The toilet cistern couldn't have filled already, so Vesuvius must have flushed another one. Another ghastly brew was on its way.

Ben did manage to climb out, but only after three of Vesuvius' pulls had discharged their evil contents over him. I didn't know what to do. I laughed alongside Ron and noticed Vesuvius framed in the light of the police station door.

"Have they come through?" he called.

There was no reply from the sorry man. It was at that moment that the telephone rang, so Vesuvius dashed inside to answer it and I followed. We left Ron to replace the manhole cover after helping his smelly friend out.

"Right, I'll tell them," he said, replacing the telephone as I entered.

"Malton Office," he announced to Ron. "That was Sergeant Colbeck. There's a domestic disturbance in town. You're needed there urgently, both of you."

"Now?" Ben cried.

"Straight away," Vesuvius smiled. "No. 10 Welsh Terrace."

"We've no keys!"

"Oh, I forgot," Vesuvius grinned stupidly. "There's always a spare set kept here, one set for every car in the Sub-Division and for all official cars which regularly call. Sergeant Blaketon's idea, being a belt-and-braces man. I'll get 'em," and he pottered into the sergeant's office, unlocked a drawer and lifted out a set of keys. They bore the registration number of their patrol car. "Sorry I forgot about those," he said. "It's not every station that has them — I've a bloody awful memory, you know."

"I'll clean up in the car," Ben said, the ordure dripping from him.

"You bloody well won't!" Ron snarled. "You're not getting into the car like that! You smell worse than a pigsty — what a bloody awful mess!"

"Worse than egg yolks, eh?" smiled Vesuvius. "That call was urgent, lads."

And so they had to leave. Ben hobbled to the car in bare feet and sat upon one of the rubber mats which he lifted from the floor and placed on the seat. The stench from his appalling bath was overpowering and they drove away with all windows open and Ben dripping ghastly fluids to the car floor.

Vesuvius smiled.

"They're nice lads, really," he said quietly, and then the telephone rang again.

"Eltering Police, PC Ventress," he answered. He listened for a moment and replied, "No, Sergeant. All's quiet here. Nothing doing."

He replaced the handset and turned towards me. "Fancy a coffee, son?" he asked.

CHAPTER THREE

From ghoulies and ghosties and long-leggety beasties,
And things that go bump in the night.
Good Lord, deliver us.

— ANONYMOUS

Two fears must be conquered by the constable on night-duty. The first is the fear of the dark and the second is a fear of ghosts. There are constables who are subjected to one or both of these terrors, and for them a night patrol is a continuing test of courage and devotion to duty. Happily, I have never been afraid of either and was never worried about patrolling during the hours of darkness. In fact, it was very enjoyable, even in the town, but the countryside around Aidensfield offered far more than the streets of Strensford.

The wide, open spaces of the North Yorkshire moors offered little in the way of crime, but they did produce sounds which could terrify the townsman. There might be the cry of the vixen, the scream of the barn owl, the cough of a sheep or cow and the weird sobbing sounds of wild geese flying overhead. We called the latter "Gabriel Ratchets" or "Hell's Hounds" for the older generation believed they were angels seeking the lost souls of unbaptised babies, or that they were the angels of death hovering over houses in which a death would soon occur.

Policemen, as a rule, care not for ancient legends or the vagaries of nature, and our patrols were chiefly a crime prevention exercise. The presence of our vehicle made the public aware that we were out and about during the witching hours, and this was comforting to those who considered themselves at risk. For the lonely and the frightened there is something reassuring about the presence of a mobile police officer at night. In some respects he assumes the role of the guardian angel we were taught about in childhood. He is there if he is needed.

With the passage of time every spell of uneventful night-duty conformed to a pattern. For my part, I would book on duty at Ashfordly, spend some time reading the latest horror stories featuring domestic rows, thefts, burglaries, shop-breaking or stolen cars, and having digested that unsavoury menu, I would sally forth into the market town. There I would diligently shake hands with lots of doorknobs. I would make my uniform seen by everyone who was out and about and thus create among the public the cosy feeling that the police were present and acting in their interest. We care about the communal safety of society and must make that care evident to those in our charge.

As the public houses ejected their regulars it was prudent to patrol the marketplace looking fierce as drunks fought the effects of the fresh air, but by 11 o'clock the town was usually dead. Only if the Young Farmers' Club or Ashfordly Ladies' Dining Club had organised a function did the routine vary, in which case the home-going was a little later and the drunks a little more entertaining. In addition, the duty became enjoyable for the policeman because lots of pretty girls were in a chatty and romantic mood.

When Ashfordly was finally at peace we patrolled the villages, making points in the manner I have earlier described. To the layman this must seem a mundane sort of existence and it is fair to say that the duty could be boring in the extreme. It could be crushingly monotonous. One old constable tried to cheer me up during such a period by saying, 'T' job's what thoo maks it, lad,' and with his words in my head, I learned that I could bring interest to those lonely patrols.

One way of breaking the tedium was to investigate the marvellous range of epitaphs in churchyards. A fear of ghosts and ghoulies and things that go bump in the night meant a wide gap in the education of the sufferers, and I wondered if I could make a collection of interesting inscriptions. Was there sufficient variety to justify this? I discovered that the night flew if I spent some time in the churchyards of my beat, so I took to wandering around each one for ten minutes at a time, ostensibly checking the security of the premises. By flashing my torch on a bewildering array of tombstones, I discovered some gems. There were old ones and new ones, they were carved in marble and in stone, some were ornate, others very simple. There were obelisks and tiny wooden crosses, but all contained sentiments applicable to the dear departed.

My researches revealed that the modern epitaph is a plain affair when compared with some of the older ones, and I enjoyed such beauties as:

Tread softly — if she waken, she'll talk

or

Underneath this sod lies Arabella Young
Who on 5th May began to hold her tongue.

Another read:

Here lie I, no wonder I'm dead
The wheel of a wagon went over my head.

In Whitby I found the following:

Sudden and unexpected was the end,
Of our esteemed and beloved friend,

> He gave to his friends a sudden shock
> By falling into Sunderland Dock.

And this one:

> Here lies the body of John Mound
> Who was lost at sea and never found.

In a village near Malton, there is:

> For all the pains and trouble from my birth
> All that I've gained is just my length of earth.

High in the Dales one can find:

> Think of me as you pass by,
> As you are now, so once was I.
> As I am now, some day you'll be,
> So now prepare to follow me.

Someone, perhaps a night-duty policeman, had added the following:

> To follow you I'm not content,
> I do not know which way you went.

It could be difficult to determine the most enjoyable epitaph, but this is one of my favourites:

> There was an old man who averred
> He had learned to fly like a bird.
> Cheered by thousands of people,
> He leapt from the steeple –
> This tomb states the date it occurred.

My real favourite, which is so brief and typically Yorkshire, reads:

> Beneath this sod lies another.

It was during one of those epitaph hunts that I stepped into a rather frightening situation in a graveyard. The boots I wore at night were silent and comfortable, and this enabled me to creep about unheard and unseen, a useful talent when shadowing felonious individuals. It also meant I unwittingly surprised other people and, on this occasion, I had decided to pay a short visit to the churchyard at Elsinby. It was about 10.30 at night and I had some ten minutes to kill before moving around my beat. I reckoned a quick perambulation among the tombstones would occupy those spare moments.

The lych-gate was open, which was unusual, and I wondered if there were criminals abroad. Perhaps someone had broken in to steal the valuables? Fearing the worst I crept along the stone-flagged path, alert and ready for anything, even the presence of Sergeant Blaketon. Then I heard voices speaking in low whispers and they came from behind the church. I did have intruders!

I crept forward with my spine tingling and the hair on the back of my neck standing on tiptoe. In a state of high excitement I rounded the end of the grey stone building and, in the deep shadows, I halted. I knew I was invisible if I remained motionless. I listened for more sounds, but there was nothing. I wondered if I had been mistaken, for I was sure I'd heard voices. Then I saw the vague outline of shadowy figures moving stealthily between the rows of memorials. I wondered if I had stumbled upon a coven of modern witches or someone emulating Burke and Hare. I must see more. I waited trembling slightly, and once again I could hear mumbling voices. Occasionally, lights would flash and silhouetted heads would appear and disappear before the group moved on. I had difficulty counting the heads because of their up-and-down motions, but after a few minutes of careful study I realised I was watching the congregation of the Hopbind Inn.

Gradually, recognisable voices floated across to me on the silent evening air and, having solved that problem, I wondered what on earth, or in the name of heaven, they were doing. It seemed that the entire regular population of the bar was there, creeping among the graves and muttering among themselves. I decided to perform my duty and find out what was happening. I left my place of concealment and strode purposefully to the area where they were still at work.

When I was close to them, I halted and in a loud voice demanded, "What's going on here, then?"

"Oh, it's you, Mr Rhea," said the familiar tones of Dick-the-Sick, on a visit to Elsinby. "We're looking for Dr Russell's grave."

"Dr Russell?" I was puzzled.

"Aye," chipped in another voice. "You remember. He lived in Thrush Grange years ago, a big chap who liked shooting pheasants. Died a bit back. Nice bloke."

"I never knew him," I had to admit. "It was before my time. Anyway, why is everybody looking for his grave tonight?"

"We've a bet on with George at the pub. He reckons the doctor died in 1932 and I said it was 1933. Then somebody reckoned it was summer and another told us it was early in the year, March or thereabouts. Well, we all got arguing so we put bets on. George is behind the bar, holding our money — ten bob a go. Whoever is closest gets the cash. So we're all checking. Trouble is, no one remembers which is his grave."

"I said it was March 1932," chipped in Dick, leaving me as he continued his search. I watched them with interest. Some had candles, one was using a box of matches and several had hand torches. Two of them had oil-lamps or storm lanterns. The less fortunate relied on lights provided by their colleagues and some even trusted the others to shout out the correct date. The combined effect was pretty eerie from a distance.

Eager to learn the truth I began to walk around the graveyard, shining my torch on the dates and at the same time looking for more interesting epitaphs. Together, the little group walked about that deserted place, some thirty stooping figures all shining lights on headstones. I must admit I got carried away with enthusiasm and found myself as keen as the others to learn the correct date.

Then another voice sounded close behind me.

"Rhea? What's going on? What the hell are you doing?"

It was Sergeant Blaketon. He had arrived in the village with the expectation of meeting me at the kiosk, but I had forgotten the time. He now stood tall and majestic beneath the shadows of the church, his brilliant torch shining directly at me. I walked slowly towards him, realising I was in trouble.

"Checking a date, Sergeant," I said, wondering if it sounded very stupid.

"Date? What date?"

"The death of Dr Russell, Sergeant. There's been a discussion in the pub, you see, and they're all checking . . ."

"Friday, 3rd May 1929," he said with conviction. "This is his grave." And he shone his torch on to a tomb not far from the gate. "Come on."

"It's here," I called to the villagers, shining my light on the gravestone.

With no more ado I walked out of the churchyard with Sergeant Blaketon silent and stern at my side. We stood on the kerb as the villagers all trooped past, each checking it for himself before returning to the bar. There would now be a share-out of the money and, hopefully, more drinks although it was after closing-time.

"Are they all friends of the licensee?" he asked, and I detected the faintest hint of humour in his voice. Friends of the licensee could drink after normal hours, at his expense.

"Yes, Sergeant," I said, hoping he would believe me and trusting he would not enter the bar to check the validity of that statement.

"Good," he said affably. "Now show me the castle."

We walked away in silence and turned up the long drive that leads out of the village and up to the ancient castle on the hill. "Sergeant," I deigned to ask. "How did you know that date and where to find the grave?"

"Do you read police books, Rhea?"

"Sometimes, Sergeant."

"Forensic medicine?"

"Now and again."

"Well, Dr Russell was a pioneer of modern forensic pathology. Clever chap, he was. Wrote a book about the use of forensic pathology in the field of crime detection. Worth reading, Rhea. Surely you've read *Russell on Scratch Marks*?"

"No, Sergeant, but I'll get it from the library," and I fell into silence as I marched up the drive at his side, perfectly in step with his ramrod figure. Although he said no more about Dr Russell, I got the impression from his demeanour that he was letting the village drink late in honour of the long-dead doctor who I guessed was one of Blaketon's heroes.

This incident showed me that the locals of the Hopbind Inn were an imaginative crowd, but the affair of Dr Russell's tombstone wasn't the only event which caused me problems. It is fair to say that the tombstone happening was a very minor hiccup in my parochial patrolling and, in comparison, the laying of the Elsinby ghost was almost disastrous.

Legend assured us that the ghost of Sir Nicholas Fairfax, a long-dead occupant of Elsinby Castle, walked the village at certain times. His appearance, clad in the dark armour which was his symbol, occurred only when the midnight full moon coincided with the midnight of the anniversary of his death. The chances of those events happening together were considerably remote and a local mathematician once attempted to calculate the dates when this would occur. He failed because he got drunk on the free drinks supplied at the Hopbind Inn during his attempt.

It was fortuitous that the anniversary of Nicholas Fairfax's death and a full moon happened to coincide during one of my spells of night-duty. I was blissfully unaware of this momentous event and was patrolling the village during the hours of darkness in my usual manner. The inhabitants of the Hopbind Inn, however, had anticipated this accident of history and had been discussing it at length in the bar. One of the customers was Dick-the-Sick who had been paying one of his regular visits to Elsinby from Aidensfield. As had happened on previous occasions the regulars had plied him with drink and had talked him into taking action he would otherwise have avoided.

This background information was later supplied to me, but I include it here in order to retain the sequence of events. It seems that the locals of the Hopbind Inn were relating the stirring deeds of the brave, handsome Sir Nicholas and told how he met his untimely death. In the hushed atmosphere of the pub there followed the story of the ghost which appeared on such rare occasions.

The reaction from the bar was mixed, to say the least. The older customers swore that it happened — they *knew* that the ghost did appear. Newcomers to the area and young people pooh-poohed the idea, saying there were no such things as ghosts let alone one that celebrated its owner's death by the light of the moon. The discussion raged long and fierce over full and frothy pints, and as the night wore on, there arose the question of people's fear of ghosts. Among the loud voices raised in the bar that night was the familiar sound of Dick-the-Sick. He swore he was not afraid of any ghost. He didn't believe in them, and he was not afraid of anything which pretended to be a ghost, even if it was a long-dead knight clad in black armour who walked by the light of the full moon.

A bold, definitive statement of that kind from Dick was like manna from heaven. As one, the customers turned upon the poor chap and coaxed him into proving his fearlessness. They plied him liberally with a fiery mixture of beer and whisky and persuaded him to prove his valour. His test would be at the ancient packhorse bridge which spanned the River Elsin at a point not far from the approach road to the castle. The ghost of Sir Nicholas crossed it at midnight when it appeared, and the locals told of the ghostly manifestation which walked from the castle towards the field where the bold knight had met his death by the light of the silvery moon. So horrible was the spectre that no one dared go near the bridge to test the truth of the legend.

It was no surprise to the packed bar that Dick found himself volunteering to watch the bridge that night, at midnight. Dick reassured everyone that he would do just that. He would settle the issue once and for all. Loud cheers greeted this announcement and it seemed yet another occasion to justify the unofficial extension of hours. It was the noise of this minor celebration which attracted my attention as I entered Elsinby that fateful evening.

I walked into the situation like an innocent child stepping off the footpath in London's Regent Street. It would be around 11.15 when I entered the village to see the pub lights blazing and the populace in full song. Closing-time was 10.30, so I entered the pub slowly and, like John Wayne might have done, thrust open the bat-wings of the saloon. Everyone fell silent at the sight of the uniform.

I looked at my watch, making the one-armed gesture very slowly as I stared in official distaste at the landlord, George.

"Pint?" he asked.

"Come off it, George!" I retorted. "You know it's past closing-time. There's no extension. Put the cloth over the handles and let's be having you out, all of you. Everyone go home quietly."

There followed the inevitable lull and looks of utter disbelief at my words. It seemed almost criminal to close a pub in this village, but George obeyed and draped the covers over the pump-handles, the signal that drinking had ceased. Then Dick-the-Sick pushed himself forward with an almost empty glass of evil-smelling fluid in his hands and said, "Ah'ssh goin' to sshoot the ghossht, Misshter Rhea," he grinned widely at this announcement. "Old Nick, down at the bridge, tonight . . ."

"What ghost?"

George came to the rescue. "There's an old legend, Mr Rhea, that the ghost of Sir Nicholas Fairfax walks across Elsinby Bridge at midnight on the anniversary of his death, but only when it coincides with the full moon. That's tonight, you see, because he died by the light of the moon. He walks down from the castle and across the river to the field where he was killed by a rival."

"Really?" I tried to sound convinced.

My scepticism caused several of the locals to join an attempt to convince me, and in the end George vanished into the private rooms of his inn and returned with an ancient volume. He opened it at a stained page bearing a drawing of an armour-clad knight striding across the old bridge. There was a full moon in the background and the caption supported their yam.

"Ah'sssh goin' to sshhoot it . . ." and Dick vanished from the inn.

There followed some loud and heated discussion about the veracity of the story, and I must admit we all forgot about Dick and his shotgun. As the controversy raged, I realised it was quarter to twelve, and I had a point at the village kiosk at midnight. It was time for me to leave.

"We're all going to watch the bridge," George told me as I made my move to leave the inn. "Coming?"

"I've a point at midnight," I said by way of an excuse.

"The telephone box is just a few yards from the bridge," he informed me as if I didn't know that already. "You'd hear it ring if they wanted you."

"Aye, all right," I agreed, for it would be an interesting diversion for me.

In typical Hopbind Inn fashion, every customer in the bar emerged and made their way along the dark byways towards Elsinby Bridge. The bridge was little used because it was too narrow for the modern motorcar, although foot passengers, visitors in particular, did enjoy its ancient, arched beauty. The track ran alongside the stream and provided numerous vantage points among the shrubbery and vegetation. I reckoned there must have been thirty customers concealed along that river bank, all squatting in the darkness on stones and grassy areas, watching the hump-backed bridge.

I sat on my haunches beside a man whose name I did not know, and in deathly silence we watched the graceful outline.

The bridge rose high above the water, rising aesthetically from each bank to its peak above the centre of the water. The route across was very rough and cobbled, but it was a beautiful construction, the work of many hours of hard labour. As we sat by the side of that bubbling stream, the full moon broke from the dark clouds and cast its green lights across the entire landscape. It was almost as light as day and yet the gloom about the shrubbery totally concealed the ghost spotters.

If the legend was correct, the ghostly knight would step on to the bridge at the far side and cross towards us, en route to the grassy fields behind. He must be almost due. I looked at my watch. It was three minutes to midnight, three minutes to the ghost's walk, three minutes to my point time. As I waited, I wondered if Sergeant Blaketon or even the Superintendent would pay me a visit. Absence from a point was inexcusable, but I didn't want to leave here, not now. I must learn the truth of the legend. Risking my career, I stayed put.

Behind us, life in the village appeared normal. The occasional courting cat howled, and cars passed through with muffled roars, then the peaceful picture was blessed by the cheery sounds of the parish church clock striking twelve. It began to boom out its twelve strokes, laboriously recording the irrevocable passage of time, and as I counted every slow note, I kept my eyes glued on that bridge. There was not a murmur, not a movement, from the assembled witnesses . . . nine . . . ten . . . eleven . . . twelve! Midnight.

As the final stroke echoed and died away, a small cloud slid across the moon and a dark shadow was cast across the water. For the watchers it was like someone switching off a light or blowing out a candle. It was all over, and the ghost had not appeared, although there was a distant eeriness as a cool wind appeared as if from nowhere and fluttered across the surface of the stream. Its passage whipped up tiny wavelets and rustled the grass and leaves. I shivered. Then followed a long, deep silence as the wind dropped. There was a total, stifling silence. The tension was indescribable, but why?

"Good God!" breathed a voice behind me. "Look . . ."

And there in the gloom at the far side of the water was the dark ghostly figure of the knight. It moved slowly and with great precision, a tall, upright figure gliding smoothly and purposefully from the shadows of the trees and mounting the rising slope of the bridge. We saw only his top half — the legs and waist were concealed by the parapets and the cloudy darkness made the moving spectre very indistinct. But it was certainly there. No one could deny it.

"I wouldn't have believed it!" breathed a voice close to me. "I bloody well wouldn't . . ."

Then there was pandemonium.

The spell was broken by the crash of twigs and branches, accompanied by a nervous shout and immediately followed by the crash of an exploding twelve-bore shotgun. It came from the far side of the beck, and the figure on the bridge instantly vanished. I was aware of a running figure on the other side of the river, but I got up and ran to the bridge.

Suddenly I forgot about spectres and ghostly creatures for I wanted to cross the river to catch the poacher at the other side. I was sure I'd got myself a poacher, but as I crested the summit of the tiny, short bridge my waving torch picked out the figure of Sergeant Blaketon. He was crouching and quivering with fear behind the shelter of the stone parapet.

"Rhea? Thank God!" he panted. "I was shot at."

"Poachers, I think, Sergeant," I managed to say, panting slightly. I was thinking fast. "I was on the other side, watching. I don't think he was shooting at you."

By now the others had materialised from their hiding places and were gingerly standing at our side of the bridge as I helped Oscar to his feet.

"It's the sergeant," I shouted at them. "He's okay. I think that poacher took fright, lads. He's gone."

George came to my rescue.

"We'll catch the sod one day," he said. "Come on, lads. Back home."

It wasn't difficult to assure Sergeant Blaketon we had been lying in wait to ambush a local poacher, saying we believed it to be a chap from another village. The suspect had eluded police, gamekeepers and residents alike, so we'd joined forces to catch him. Oscar seemed to accept this because the area around the bridge was noted for its profusion of pheasants which roosted in the trees. We all expressed the feeling that the timely arrival of Sergeant Blaketon had terrified the poachers who'd run off, accidentally discharging their guns, or one of them, as they ran. One could tolerate one's own poachers, but not those from neighbouring areas.

Blaketon and I examined the ground near the end of the bridge and found signs in the earth which suggested a premature discharge of a shotgun at close range. Our theory was thus borne out.

Sometime later I learned that Dick-the-Sick had literally taken fright upon the ghostly appearance of Sergeant Blaketon and had run off in terror. In the darkness and in his haste he had tripped over his gun which had been accidentally triggered off. Blaketon never knew this, of course, and I was thankful for Dick's fear.

When it was all over, and the men had dispersed to their homes Sergeant Blaketon and myself spent about an hour searching for the poachers but drew a blank. I felt a bit of a twit, searching in this way, but had little alternative. Finally, we adjourned to his car, where he produced his notebook, patted his pocket and said,

"Blast! My pen! My fountain pen! It's gone."

"Maybe you lost it on the bridge, Sergeant?"

"Let's have a look."

We returned to the ancient bridge and, by the light of my torch, searched thoroughly for his fountain pen. He told me it was a present to him when he left his previous job to join the police force years ago, and he was sentimentally attached to it.

Fortunately, I found the pen lying in a gully upon the bridge, very close to where I had found him crouching. I picked it up, handed it to him and said, "It's been a lucky night for you, Sergeant."

I meant it.

We turned and walked off the bridge and I was very content. It had been an interesting night. But, as we left, a cool breeze suddenly rustled the leaves and I shivered. It grew very cold and the village clock struck one. At that instant I chose to take a last look at the old bridge and my action caused Oscar Blaketon to turn his head too. In the back of my mind I was wondering how good a target he had been, and he turned to see what I was staring at.

And there, walking over Elsinby Bridge by the light of the moon, was a tall dark figure in a plumed helmet.

He said nothing. Neither did I, although I did wonder what William Willett and our altered clocks had to do with it. I couldn't decide. The intricacies of Greenwich Mean Time, British Summer Time and Central European Time were a little too confusing for me at that time of night.

But I often wonder who walked across the bridge.

Being practical types most policemen are not easily scared by rumour or fact and they treat ghosts for what they are — flimsy creatures who could never harm anyone other than to send cool shivers down the spine or give rise to legends in pubs. There are exceptions, of course, because some police officers are terrified of ghosts.

Lanky Leonard Lazenby of Eltering Police Station was such a man. He was terrified of ghosts. The mere thought of them caused him to palpitate alarmingly and it was his misfortune to break into a cold sweat at the beginning of every period of night-duty. He had a dread of meeting a ghost during his patrol, a fact which was very evident to the other members of his shift. Some sergeants, however, were models of consideration and would arrange the station duties so that poor Leonard was given office work or alternatively patrolled the town centre, which was illuminated for most of the night. This arrangement was not out of deep compassion for Leonard — it was a means by which the job continued to be done because a panic-stricken constable is of little or no value, with or without ghosts. It was sensible to allocate him to a duty where he was of some use instead of being a gibbering wreck all night.

Periodically, however, Leonard's weakness was overlooked when a relief sergeant compiled the duty-sheet. These newcomers were usually ignorant of Leonard's propensity to tremble at the sound of a fluttering leaf, and so it transpired that Sergeant Charlie Bairstow was allocated the task of being night-shift sergeant for the Eltering Sub-Division.

He had often caused embarrassment to me and it seems, on reflection, that he was aware of Leonard's *other* great fear.

If there was one creature that Leonard feared more than a ghost it was the Superintendent. Superintendents of every kind terrified Lanky Leonard Lazenby. This combination of factors coincided one late autumn night when I was on duty in Eltering.

Leonard was also on patrol in the town and I was performing one of my motorised merry-go-rounds in the surrounding landscape. Another happy fact was that Ben and Ron, the terrible traffic twins, were also on night-duty, carrying out their routine motor patrols. That night we sat in the office, munching our sandwiches and telling stories. Sergeant Bairstow took the chair normally reserved for Vesuvius, who was enjoying a rest day, and Leonard and I listened to the high-spirited pair and the sergeant as they entertained us.

Those night-shift meal breaks were relaxing and enjoyable, and sometimes extended more than the permitted three-quarters of an hour. On this occasion Leonard had come in for his break at 1.30 am, which meant he was due out at 2.15 am. I had come in at 1.45 am with Sergeant Bairstow, and the two traffic lads had entered at 2 am. Nonetheless, we formed a happy, laughing group.

As 2.15 am approached, Bairstow turned to Leonard and said, "Well, Len, it's time to go. Do the second half of seven beat tonight, will you? I've heard the Superintendent will be out early. He's doing one of his morning prowls, trying to catch us out, so we'll be prepared for him."

"Yes, Sergeant," said Leonard, his face as pale and as fragile as French chalk.

As Leonard worried about this instruction I noticed a sly glance pass between Bairstow and the two traffic men but failed to read anything significant into it at the time. Like everyone else I knew of Leonard's terror of dark places and of his pathological dread of superintendents. I realised that seven beat embraced the castle, its ancient chapel and grave-yard, and the long winding and dark footpath through dense woodland to a Forestry Commission workman's hut high on the moors. Inside was a telephone, chair and table, with an oil lamp. There was nothing else. The place was never locked and was regarded as a sort of refuge for lonely or lost folks on the hills, for workmen, for holidaymakers, lovers or even patrolling policemen who had to make points.

To reach this tiny wooden shelter from Eltering it was necessary to climb the steep flight of steps which led towards the castle and then walk through the adjoining graveyard. A stone-flagged footpath twisted among the ancient tomb-stones and emerged at the far side where it led straight into the forest and along the unmade road towards the cabin. It was customary for the Superintendent to meet the beat man at the cabin at the weirdest possible hours. He seemed to enjoy the task of keeping us alert to the fact that he was likely to turn up here at any time of the day or night. I have yet to understand why we had to make a point here, but we did.

Tonight it seemed as if the Superintendent was going to make one of his check calls.

That thought sent poor old Leonard scurrying along that route at the dead of night. His fear of superintendents had superseded his dread of ghosts but had not obliterated it. Thus he had two fears to contend with as he made his silent way towards that isolated point in the forest. I felt a twinge of concern for Leonard as he began his perilous journey.

When Leonard had left the office, Sergeant Bairstow smiled at Ben and Ron.

"Okay?" was all he said.

"Fine," Ben replied, and after another twenty minutes they also left.

I was now alone with Sergeant Bairstow.

"Well, Nicholas," he said affably. "It's been a quiet night, eh? No trouble? Nothing stirring."

"Very quiet, Sergeant," I agreed.

"You've never been to that hut, have you? The Forestry Commission Place?"

"No, I haven't," I agreed.

"The local foot patrols go there. It's not really on the beats of you lads from rural patches," he told me. "You can't get a car far along the track although the Super sometimes manages. He wouldn't do it if it was his own private car!"

"Does he often meet men there?" I asked. "It seems a strange place for him to worry about."

"He's a strange man," smiled Bairstow. "Right, let's go. Leave your car — take a walk with me. I'll show you the castle, the ruined chapel and the graveyard."

"Thanks," I was looking forward to the break from routine but puzzled by his actions. Why show me this? It wasn't on my beat tonight and anyway, Lanky Leonard would be braving the dark to cope with problems in that part of the Sub-Division.

I locked the office and allowed the friendly sergeant to guide me to the lonely Forestry Commission hut. We sauntered casually through the deserted streets and chattered in low voices as he led me towards the outskirts of the market town. Finally he took me through a thicket which led into woodland. As we climbed the steep, shadowy path, I could see the gaunt outline of Eltering Castle over to my right. The lighter areas of night sky revealed the battered outline of this interesting place and in true Dracula style a barn owl floated on silent white wings from the ramparts and glided over our heads as we moved stealthily towards the grounds.

"Don't make a sound," whispered Sergeant Bairstow. "There's something I want you to see up there."

I puzzled over this as his measured tread became lighter. He strode ahead of me, tripping through the quiet avenues of trees until we entered the grounds of the ruined castle by climbing over a low drystone wall. I followed, hardly daring to breathe. Whatever lay in here must be very important and interesting because Sergeant Bairstow was creeping silently across the carefully cut turf and heading for the far side of the grounds. I followed as he padded across the emptiness of the ruin and eventually came to a small iron gate. It was closed but not locked, and he opened it. It squeaked faintly as we passed through and I found myself in a graveyard, somewhat overgrown but adjoining an isolated and ruined chapel.

A small church stood beside it and I knew the church did accommodate services from time to time. Certain Eltering families had ancient rights of burial here for this was their parish church. Some had their own pews too.

Charlie Bairstow led me through the deep grass, weaving between the assorted gravestones which stood at every conceivable angle. Finally we came to rest near a sturdy obelisk mounted on a series of steps and surmounted by a cross.

"All right?" he hissed.

"Fine," I said, breathing heavily after the tension of trying to be very quiet.

"Just watch," he bade me, and I saw him lift his torch and flash it once or twice across the graveyard. I was surprised to see an answering beam from the depths of the distant shadows.

"Fine," said Bairstow with no explanation.

There was a long pause during which he looked at his watch and eventually he whispered, "See that path through the churchyard, over to your right?"

"Yes," I could see it.

"It goes down to Eltering and emerges near the bus station. That's the way the bobby comes on his route to the Forestry Commission hut. We took a short cut."

"Oh," I said as if understanding his conversation.

"The hut is across to our left, a few minutes' walk into that forest," and I turned my head to see the tall, slender, pointed outlines of the conifers which formed the forest.

Then there was some movement. He hissed for silence and squatted behind the sheltering base of the obelisk. I did likewise, albeit keeping my eyes on the scene ahead. My sight had become accustomed to the pale darkness and I could see that we were very close to the path which bisected the graveyard before leading into the woods. Beyond, at the far side, were more rows of dilapidated tombstones, some showing white in the darkness, and I was sure the torch flash had come from near one of them. I wondered if I was involved in an important observation exercise, perhaps lying in wait for a criminal? Maybe the local police had received a tip about something unlawful? A visit by a graveyard vandal, maybe? A robber of the Burke and Hare variety? A writer-on-tombstones? Someone hiding loot from the proceeds of crime? The handing over of stolen property? The range of possibilities was almost endless.

It was quite exciting really, waiting in the darkness with an experienced officer at my side and learning first-hand the art of catching villains and ne'er-do-wells. I was looking forward to the outcome of this strange excursion.

Then someone was coming. I heard the sounds. A tall figure materialised over to our right, coming from the direction of Eltering town. The darkness made it difficult to see him properly, but the anonymous person walked very slowly into the graveyard and began to cross it. I waited, my heart thumping. A crook? A night prowler of some sort?

The figure halted. Sergeant Bairstow cursed under his breath and I heard him mutter to himself, "Go on . . . do it . . ."

A crime of some kind was about to be committed. I knew the value of witnessing the actual commission of a crime rather than trying to convince a court that the man had attempted to commit something unlawful. There's a world of difference between an intent and an attempt, and another world of difference between an attempt and the full commission of an unlawful act. No doubt Charlie Bairstow wanted this character to prove himself a wrong 'un, then he'd pounce to effect a very smart arrest.

As the sergeant crouched at the base of the obelisk I looked into the gloom, trying to spot anyone else. The torch signal told me that someone lurked out there and I guessed it was the CID, although it could be a uniformed officer from Malton.

Sergeant Bairstow's eyes were still firmly fixed on the slow-moving figure across to our right. The figure was still motionless. It was stalemate.

As Sergeant Bairstow appeared to be in command of the situation I looked around for other villains, hoping to contribute by spotting the approach of his mates. I looked around carefully and as my glance rested on the gate which led into the woods, I saw someone. My heart leapt.

There *was* another figure; he was standing very close to the gateposts and appeared to be hiding from the man on the footpath. He was just within my view. I could distinguish the pale face, although his clothing was so dark that it was impossible to see any more of him. An occasional movement betrayed him; sometimes I saw the white of his hand as he examined his watch and I thought about notifying his presence to the sergeant, but I felt I should not interfere in this operation. Besides, any movement or noise from me could spoil the whole thing. After all, I was a mere observer in what was clearly a carefully planned police operation. Every detail would have been considered and every participant well briefed about his role.

Eventually the tall, slow-moving figure who was the focal point of the exercise came forward a few more paces. His hesitancy seemed to be evaporating and his confidence was growing. He seemed to accept that he had a nerve-jangling mission to complete and began to stride purposefully across the quiet churchyard, heading for the concealed man behind the gate. The meeting was nigh. I could feel the tension, especially in Sergeant Bairstow. He hardly dared to breathe.

When the man reached a point directly in front of Sergeant Bairstow and myself, Bairstow whispered, "This is it, Nicholas!"

I watched intently, holding my breath. The excitement was electric.

Suddenly there was a ghastly shriek and I saw the earth move. A dim light appeared from the base of a tombstone directly across the path from our position, and I saw a horrible white face rise from the grave. A blood-red light accentuated the eye sockets and nostrils. It was an awful sight.

With a sharp cry the tall figure turned and ran. I saw him galloping the way he had come, and at that point Charlie Bairstow burst into fits of laughter. The tall, running figure vanished through the gate and could be heard crashing his way through the undergrowth towards the town.

Holding his sides with laughter giving pain and pleasure together Charlie Bairstow left his hiding place and walked across to the scene of the apparition, laughing uproariously. I went with him, shaken but interested in what had happened.

My heart was pounding after the sudden shock but there before us were Ben and Ron, chuckling to themselves. Ben's face was smothered in white flour and the two traffic men doubled up with laughter as they saw us.

It had been a well-planned joke against poor Lanky Leonard.

I examined the scene. Covering one of the old graves at the side of the path was a large square piece of theatrical grass, a green mat-like material. It was the kind of stuff used in showrooms or upon the stage to simulate a grassy area and in the darkness looked most realistic. Ron had concealed himself behind the tombstone while Ben had lain full length upon the grave of some long-dead character. The grass-green coverlet had hidden him; with his face powdered a deathly white he had lain there with his hands crossed upon his breast, clutching the torch. At a shriek signal from Ron he had switched on the light. With the lens covered with a piece of red glass the light had shone from beneath the coverlet to spotlight his horrible face, shining from directly beneath his chin. Thus illuminated Ben had slowly raised himself into a sitting position with the green coverlet pinned to his tunic under the chin.

From a distance it had looked for all the world like a corpse rising from its tomb and not the ideal sight for a highly nervous person like Leonard.

Sergeant Bairstow and I had a good laugh, while Ben and Ron thought the whole episode hilarious. Charlie Bairstow had done it again — he had deliberately allocated this beat to poor Lanky Leonard, knowing his fear of ghosts and his even greater fear of the Superintendent. No one will ever know the conflict in Leonard's mind as he struggled with his decisions that night. From his point of view it must have been horrifying and I must admit to a certain sympathy with him as he galloped to safety. It transpired he had gone straight home to report his going off duty, sick — suffering from diarrhoea.

After the episode Ben and Ron returned to the office, taking us with them in their police car. Over a cup of congratulatory coffee we relived the prank which, I knew, would enter the annals of remarkable police legends.

As we laughed and talked, I remembered the other person who'd been at the woodland gate. Who was that? He wasn't here, celebrating with us.

"Who was that other chap?" I asked amid the laughter and gaiety.

"Other chap?" cried Charlie Bairstow. "What other chap?"

"At the top gate, the one leading into the Forestry Commission land. He was standing there just before Ben did his stuff. I saw him."

"Are you sure?" Charlie asked. "What was he like? Who was it?"

"I dunno," I had to admit. "It was somebody in dark clothing, hiding just outside the gate. I thought it was one of our lot."

"Bloody hell!" he groaned. "I wonder who it was?"

We racked our brains before resuming patrol, and I realised I still had not been to the mysterious Forestry Commission hut. There was always another time for that pleasure.

The next night, however, I knew the identity of the mystery observer.

The Superintendent had reported sick, ostensibly suffering from a stomach complaint.

CHAPTER FOUR

The learn'd is happy nature to explore.
The fool is happy that he knows no more.
ALEXANDER POPE — *An Essay on Man*

The country policeman spends a lot of time walking close to nature and, in the still of the sleeping hours, there is much to see and hear. Wild animals and birds appear to accept the presence of man at night in a way they would never tolerate during the daytime. Perhaps this is not an accurate assessment, but it certainly appeared to be true during my sojourns into the countryside of darkness. In some ways I was conscious of being an invader in their territory and yet their objections were never more than a mere whimper or a muffled cry of alarm. It is tolerance of this kind which makes one feel very humble and very sorrowful for the way man has treated nature in the past, and the way he will treat her in the future.

Although a good deal of my night-duty was spent in and around small market towns I did spend many hours among the pine forests, moorland heights and green valleys, either performing a routine patrol or engaged upon a specific inquiry or observation of some kind. I enjoyed these very much.

I spent one night, for example, in a draughty barn keeping observations regarding a potato thief. The farmer, an interesting character called Bainbridge, cultivated a remote place on the outskirts of Briggsby and stored his season's potatoes in a large, open barn. The spuds accumulated there to await collection by a local merchant, but over a period it was clear that someone was sneaking in and stealing them by the sacksful. One sack every week disappearing but unfortunately there was no pattern to the thefts. It was difficult organising observations while engaged on so many other duties away from my beat, although I did deign to spend the occasional overnight stint in his barn. I hoped the potato pincher would enable me to arrest him red-handed.

One chilly night in late autumn, therefore, I informed Mr Bainbridge that I would inhabit his barn from midnight until three o'clock in the morning for the purpose of spud-watching. Thoughtfully, he provided me with a massive sandwich of bread and cheese, an apple pie cooked by his wife and a quarter bottle of whisky, while I armed myself with my packed supper, a flask of coffee and a torch. It promised to be a long, boring vigil although food would not be in short supply.

Inside the barn I settled among the neatly arranged sacks and found a position out of the draughts, one which provided adequate views of the various entrances. For a time my potato-filled seat was quite cosy, but the chill night air soon began to eat into my bones. I took several short walks to maintain the circulation of my blood, but it was a long, cold duty and I was never cosy.

During my time in the barn I became aware of the intense animal activity in and around the place. Sitting immobile in the darkness, I could hear furtive scuffling and scratchings of all kinds, the sound of tiny creatures running about the dusty floor or investigating the sacks for morsels of food. High-pitched squeaks came from distant corners and I guessed they were mice or shrews.

Now and again, I flashed my torch in the direction of those sounds but seldom spotlighted anything. They were too quick for me.

I discovered a large brown rat which scuttled away as my light struck its eyes, and once or twice I lit upon the scampering figures of mice, busy about their night-time chores. Cats were frequent visitors too, and if anything, they were more alert than the creatures of the wild, scattering into the farmyard outside at the slightest hint of danger. A fox came too; I heard his approach because some nervous poultry in a nearby henhouse clucked their alarm as he sniffled and snuffled around their home. He knocked a bucket so that its handle rattled, but that didn't seem to scare him off as he continued to investigate the flap of the henhouse. I listened and guessed it was Reynard, my supposition being proved correct when he entered the barn.

I noticed his slouching gait as he cautiously entered the open barn, a dark, agile figure against a patch of light in the doorway. Then I flicked on my torch. I caught him squarely and bathed him in the light which highlighted his russet coat, his bushy tail with its white tip and those sharp, greenish eyes which glowed quickly against the beam. In a trice he was gone. He vanished as suddenly as he had come, and I never saw him again.

On one occasion a barn owl flew right across my line of vision, its soft white underparts almost ghostlike as it moved silently in one door and out at the other side, doubtless hunting mice and other small creatures. Bats fluttered around too, albeit not many. These were pipistrelles, our smallest resident bat and they would be hunting late-night flying insects and finding their way around the pillars and contents of the barn by their remarkable system of radar. At times the place was filled with their squeaking cries.

In spite of the chilliness and the hours of inactivity it was a fascinating session of duty because nature came so close to me. The problem was that the thief didn't! I spent several nights in that barn but never saw him. Happily, he never came again. Maybe he was a local character who knew of my interest. I'll never know, but it does seem that my vigilance was rewarded because there were no further thefts from that barn or indeed from the village.

My night-time country walks were equally enchanting. I have observed deer, foxes, otters, rats, mice, insects and a multitude of birds. I have found baby hares squeaking for their mums at my arrival, mother jackdaws nesting in ruined buildings, rabbits with their legs caught in snares and river birds with cruel fishing hooks stuck into their flesh, throats or feet; I've found nests of baby birds and lairs of baby animals and I've discovered dead animals of every kind, many having perished pointlessly at the hand of man. There is little doubt that man is nature's greatest enemy.

Of all the wild animals that I have witnessed at night, Belinda the badger is the most memorable. I called her Belinda because I felt she needed a name.

We first met on a lonely and minor road between Elsinby and Ploatby. I had parked the police car in a small complex of buildings at the side of the lane in order to enjoy a half-hour stroll. Such strolls were necessary because the eyes and ears of a policeman on foot are infinitely better than the headlights of a car when seeking villains or preventing crime.

That lovely lane is bordered on one side by young Scots pines and on the other by low-lying fields. It is a long, winding road, but I could walk into the heart of Ploatby and return to the car in time to make my one o'clock point at Elsinby kiosk.

My boots had soft crêpe soles and I walked easily and quickly along the smooth surface of the road, enjoying the exercise and fresh night air, so full of the scents of the nearby pine forest. To my left was one of the open fields and as I approached its gateway, I was aware of a creature scurrying through the corn stubble. Its progress was very noisy among the short, stiff stalks and I froze, my torch at the ready, waiting. I was about twenty yards short of the gate.

It was fascinating, watching the outline of the rapidly moving animal as it neared the gate. When it was very close, I could distinguish the unmistakable white face of the badger, so recognisable due to the black bars which run the length of the long snout. Not many humans have been privileged to see this lovely animal in its natural surroundings let alone observe it at such close quarters, and I was enchanted.

The running badger squeezed beneath the lower bar of the gate and started to cross the road directly ahead of me. Its next move was to clamber up the steep grassy verge at the far side of the road, and I could hear its sharp claws grating against the rocky surface beneath. I now decided to flash my torch because I wanted to see the badger more clearly and, as I switched on the powerful beam, it caught the fleeing animal like a spotlight.

Its broad, powerful back was a lovely silver-grey colour, the effect being produced by a mixture of grey and almost black hair. As it momentarily turned its head towards me, I saw two tiny eyes set in that long face, then its short legs carried it rapidly up the hillside towards the sheltering forest. Long body hair almost concealed its legs, making it appear to be running on castors. It moved with astonishing speed.

Still bathed in the light of my torch the badger had difficulty in clambering up the steepening slope for it was a portly animal, but my presence and my annoying light spurred it to greater efforts. It reached the top and was then confronted by a tall wire fence topped with two strands of barbed wire. I hadn't realised the fence was there.

The badger leapt at the barrier. I switched off my torch, not wishing to alarm it any further. I had no wish to panic the animal into doing something stupid, and I hoped it would not get its head fast between the top strands. It didn't.

Instead, it managed to get itself marooned across those wires. I did wonder if the barbs had got entangled with its thick belly fur for the badger was well and truly stuck halfway across the fence. It was balancing on the centre of its stomach with its head at one side and its tail at the other. Those tiny short legs were battling to secure a foot hold upon the wire below, but they failed. They were far too short.

The result was that the badger was rocking to and fro on top of the fence, grunting and panting with frustration as it attempted to release itself from this embarrassing plight. Its long, fat body straddled the fence like a sack of flour, and I laughed involuntarily. It was almost like a Chaplin comedy.

I couldn't leave it like that. I climbed the embankment and talked soothingly, as if that would make any difference! Soon I reached a position directly behind and knowing the badger's reputation as a hard biter, I kept well clear of the snapping teeth. With both hands I lifted the rump end and toppled it over to the far side where it gathered itself, shook its entire body, and waddled high into the trees with never a backward glance or a hint of appreciation.

But that was not the end of our association.

The badger is a fascinating animal and I was delighted to learn that I had a colony of them on my beat. Almost every country dweller finds them interesting, so over the following months I made a point of travelling along that lane many times in the hope of seeing more of my local badger. Badgers are creatures of habit and I guessed that the route it had taken through the cornfield and under the gate to cross the highway had been used for many years by the local badger community.

It is this hard-headed determination to use the same route without deviation that has caused so many badger deaths. If a motorway or main road is built across a badger route, the badgers will continue to use it in spite of heavy traffic. Invariably, this has disastrous results to the badger population for they are slaughtered by fast-moving vehicles. Some thoughtful highway authorities have built badger tunnels under their roads to preserve this curious animal from further mutilation and death. This is a good example of officialdom catering for the needs of the wildlife of England.

My patience was rewarded, and I did see my badger from time to time. I did not make the mistake of shining my torch but allowed it to waddle across the road at its own pace. It always managed to clamber over the fence, achieving this without difficulty when it wasn't harassed into panic movements. I realised that the bulk of the creature was due to her pregnancy. I now knew she was a female, and she grew larger as the weeks rolled by.

My interest in the location of her home grew more intense and I began to enjoy the physical exercise of entering the wood to search for her sett, or "cett" as it is sometimes spelled. It wasn't very difficult to find because of the well-trodden path to the badger's regular route across the road. I climbed high into the trees and there near the summit of a small hillock among the scented pines, I located the badger's home.

By any standards a badger's home is a remarkable piece of construction work for this animal is perhaps the cleanest and most homely of the wild animals of England. This sett was typical for it bore the tell-tale signs of occupancy by Brock. That is the name we give to the badger in North Yorkshire, a name which features in many place names and farm addresses like Brock Rigg, Brocklesby and so forth.

The entrance nearest to me was about a yard wide and eighteen inches deep, snugly situated beneath the roots of a straggling Scots pine. The area before the hole had been paddled down into a firm, earthen base by the regular comings and goings of the family in residence. Another sign comprised many claw marks on the trunks of nearby trees, the result of badgers sharpening their claws or cleaning them. Some twenty yards away were the dung-pits. The badger does not make a mess in its living quarters but uses an outside toilet which it positions a short distance from its front door. Its cleanliness is further shown by its arrangement for other domestic waste. Down a slope was an area used to dump the waste from the interior of the home like used bedding (a heap of grass and leaves) which had been carried out and thrown a discreet distance from the entrance. In winter the female might carry the bedding out to air and then return it for further use.

I knew the inside would consist of a labyrinth of tunnels and chambers, but I could not guess how large this particular sett would be. Perhaps there were other entrances and exits, but I did not have the time to search. I was happy that I had found her sett and made my way down the hillside to my waiting car.

From time to time I returned to her crossing-place but seldom saw her. I decided then to christen her "Belinda" for reasons which now escape me, and then I saw her again. She was crossing the road in that familiar ambling gait and managed to scramble over the awkward fence. This time she appeared even heavier with cubs, and I knew that a sow could carry anything up to five young. Maybe Belinda would produce a large family.

My frequent excursions to this place revealed that she crossed the road around midnight, give or take twenty minutes either way. I knew that her route back to the sett would be the same each time, having been on a hunting expedition. Badgers enjoy their food but are not particular what they eat — insects, beetles, worms, mice, wasps and bees are all fair game, and the thick coat of this animal makes it impervious to the anger of wasps or bees when under attack. Fruit are enjoyed too, and it's not unknown for a wandering badger to scent its way into an orchard to feast upon fallen apples.

Knowing of the animal's fondness for fruit, I did wonder if I could tempt Belinda from her sett with a few choice raisins or sultanas. Badgers love these fruits and I had heard tales of country folk making friends with them by using this bait. The badger is a one-man beast, however, and such a friendship can be somewhat tenuous.

Feeling there was little to lose and a lot to gain, I began one of my night-duty patrols with a pocketful of raisins and later made my way to the edge of the sett before the usual time of Belinda's evening stroll. I placed a handful of raisins near the entrance and adjourned to a nearby hiding place. It would be very foolish to shine my torch upon the mouth of the sett, so I relied on my night sight and was eventually rewarded by the grunting approach of the stout lady. She was grumbling and puffing as, heavy with cubs, she climbed the slope towards her sett. As she approached the entrance, she smelled the goodies and was clearly suspicious. I'm sure she'd never before been presented with foreign fruit, but, after a couple of exploratory sniffs, she devoured them happily and vanished inside.

For a time this became a regular night excursion for me, both on and off duty. Each time I would drop a handful of raisins near the entrance and watch her enjoy them. Sometimes I would speak aloud from my hiding place, talking to her as I had the day I helped her over the fence. The sound of my voice did not appear to alarm her, and I began to wonder if she would respond to the raisins if I was closer to them. Maybe she already knew their presence was the work of humans. Maybe she knew I was there.

By now she was very heavy, and I guessed birth was imminent. Spring was just around the corner as February moved along with its usual dose of rain and chill. Badger cubs are usually born in February and I knew that a happy event was expected very soon in this sett. I decided to test her tameness.

One night while on patrol I placed a handful of raisins outside the sett and squatted nearby within what I reckoned was well within the range of her scent. The night was dark, albeit not pitch black, and I could see the sett entrance quite clearly. The raisins were in a small heap in their usual place, but nothing happened. Time dragged. My feet grew cold and I wondered if Sergeant Blaketon would be looking for me; maybe he'd find the parked car and wonder why it was deserted in such a remote place! I could always tell him I was seeking poachers . . .

Then she emerged. The distinctive grunting noise alerted me and suddenly her long snout appeared from the darkness below ground. She was quite visible due to the bright black-and-white pattern on her face. Without stopping she lumbered into the open air, sniffed at the raisins and began to eat. I spoke in a soft voice; she started, looked up briefly, but continued to eat. Undeterred, she gobbled up the tasty morsels with her piggy eyes fixed on me: I did not know whether she could see me, so I remained motionless, all the time talking soothingly to her. In my presence she consumed every morsel.

When she finished, I dug into my pocket and produced more, tossing them before her. I thought she would take fright and run but she didn't. She looked at me then nibbled the extra helping. I threw more, closer to me this time and she came forward.

I had heard a lot about the ferocity of an angry badger and knew that one bite from those strong jaws could fracture my wrist or severely injure me, but I also knew of their trust in man. The badger is possibly unique among wild animals because it has no natural enemies in this country, its only foe being man. Man has tortured and destroyed badgers for centuries, sometimes under the name of sport and sometimes out of sheer ignorance of their value to the countryside. For example, badger-baiting was once a common sport. In this bit of fun a badger was tied to a post and had his jaw fractured; dogs were then turned upon him to tear him to pieces and in spite of his handicaps the mutilated animal would give the bloodthirsty spectators value for their dirty money.

Today the threat comes from hunters armed with fearsome badger tongs, long steel tools which are thrust into the setts to drag the seized victim to the surface where it is shot. Badger pelts have been used to make fur coats, their fur also making useful shaving-brushes and their heads have been fashioned into sporrans. In addition, many are killed simply for the fun of it and some are slaughtered because it is feared they spread bovine tuberculosis among cattle.

In spite of everything a badger will still befriend a man. But Belinda was safe from all this, at least for the time being. But was I safe from her? Did pregnancy make the sows dangerous? I talked softly, throwing more raisins to the ground and she took them all. She came closer, not as cautiously as

I had anticipated. My heart was thumping as I tempted her to my hand. She moved slowly but clearly loving the raisins; she was very wary of me as I froze in my squatting position. I was literally inches from the pregnant sow.

Then I found I had run out of raisins. I scraped a dozen or so left in the corners of my pocket and placed them hopefully in the palm of my hand. I held them out for her, hoping the scent of my nervousness would not alarm her. It didn't.

Those narrow little eyes, close to the front of her snout, peered at me as she calmly nibbled the goodies from my hand. Then, quite abruptly, she turned and ambled off to seek more natural foods. I watched her go and lost her in the gloom although I could hear her noisy progress through the undergrowth. Finally everything was silent.

It was an amazing experience and I will never forget those precious seconds when she came so close to me, apparently without fear. I returned many more times to the sett during the following days but didn't see her. I knew the reason. She would be giving birth to her youngsters and looking after them. I wasn't sure whether the cubs remained in the sett for long periods or whether the parents took them out to learn the vital craft of survival. I had never seen the boar, although I must admit the difference in the sexes is not easy for humans to determine. The only real guide is that the adult boar's head is flatter and wider than that of his lady companion.

During the spring I paid several return visits during the midnight hours but didn't see Belinda. There was no sign of her on the road either and I began to wonder whether she had fallen foul of some badger hunter or been knocked down by a passing car. I searched the locality for signs of a carcass but found none.

Then one balmy night in early summer I decided to walk up to her sett. It was very mild and light, a typical summer's night in June and I was not even wearing a tunic. I was dressed in shirtsleeves and police trousers, but I had my torch and, optimistically, my pocket was full of raisins. The sett still bore signs of being occupied and I felt sure she was there. I placed a handful of raisins outside the entrance and settled down for one of those long vigils. This time it was reasonably pleasant, as the night was so mild.

All about me were the night sounds of summer. Insects were busy among the trees, an owl hooted somewhere beyond my vision and there were countless unidentifiable sounds within the woodland. Little animals scurried about their business, perhaps investigating me, and I heard the twitter of birds disturbed by other creatures as they roosted above and around me. Among all this I sat still upon a convenient rock, watching the black mouth of the sett. Anticipation made the time pass quickly, and I must have missed at least one of my hourly points. I forgot the passage of time as I sat and listened to the night, and then the morning sun began to brighten the sky around me. It was time to leave. It was just after three o'clock.

Then there was movement. I froze.

Deep in the blackness of the miniature cavern I detected movement. I couldn't be sure what it was, but something definitely moved. I daren't budge, not now. My leg had developed pins and needles, but I dare not shift it. I was delighted when Belinda's familiar mask appeared, moving from side to side as she sniffed the air, her sensitive snout unerringly guiding her to my pile of raisins. She found them and grunted in what I took to be a note of satisfaction, and then I saw her family. Four miniatures of herself lurked in the background and as she grunted at the food, they all emerged to join the feast. They would be very handsome brocks, I knew, when they grew up.

I watched in silence and remained utterly motionless, lest I disturb this fascinating family breakfast. When they had consumed the small meal, they all looked about and sniffed the air. I'm sure they scented me but remained close to their mother, who seemed to reassure them that this alien smell was friendly. I talked softly, and the cubs all darted off but returned seconds later when I continued to speak in a low voice. I held out a handful of raisins, which Belinda took from my still hand, but the cubs did not venture so close to me. They remained behind her, clustered in a cautious knot and then as their mother continued to enjoy her early morning snack they began to play and tumble with one another, apparently oblivious of my presence.

Belinda finished her meal and I was gladdened to see her join them in a hectic five minutes of boisterous play. Then quite suddenly they all stopped, and she ambled off down the slope with her playful brood romping behind.

I never saw them again.

Many weeks later I learned that Belinda was probably the sow cub found by a local farm lad. That cub had been orphaned by dogs during a raid on a local sett and the lad, who lived in nearby Ploatby, had taken the cub home. There he had reared it with affection but had left the district soon afterwards. The cub had been returned to the wild. Reports which reached me suggested that the badger, now fully grown, was sometimes seen in the locality and fed with titbits by gamekeepers and farmers. If this was the same sow it would explain her lack of fear of me.

Later that year I found a badger's body near the roadside. I was sure it was one of Belinda's cubs because it was near their crossing-place. The badger had a fractured skull and was badly injured about the body, a casualty of a modern motorcar accident.

Although I went to the sett from time to time I never saw Belinda or her family and I often wonder what happened to them. Badgers' families occupy their homes for centuries, and I did wonder if she had met some horrific fate at the hands of an unscrupulous human animal. I will never know.

In those days, badgers were not protected by law, but in January 1974, the Badgers Act of 1973 became effective and protected this creature of whom Winston Churchill said, 'You are the most ancient of Britons'.

The badger has lived for centuries in North Yorkshire and this rural county welcomes his presence among us. It is very significant that the nation's first prosecution under that new law was undertaken within North Yorkshire, an indication of our local respect for Brock.

But I wonder if the law would have protected Belinda from her fate?

CHAPTER FIVE

He did not know that a keeper is only a poacher
turned outside in, and a poacher is a keeper
turned inside out.
CHARLES KINGSLEY — *The Water Babies*

For extremely personal reasons Claude Jeremiah Greengrass took a late stroll in Brock Rigg Wood. This is an afforested area on the hills above Aidensfield and, like much of the district, it is owned by the Forestry Commission. Members of the public are permitted to walk along its tree-lined roads for the purpose of birdwatching or nature study, and the procedure is to obtain the requisite pass from the local office. This document must be produced upon demand to anyone authorised to ask for sight of it.

So far as I know, Claude Jeremiah did not possess such a document and indeed that was not the kind of formality that would unduly worry him. He rarely bothered with licences of any kind. His woodland stroll in the small hours of a September morning was destined to involve me because I was engaged upon one of my periods of night-duty.

The trouble started when Claude Jeremiah found a set of antlers lying on the ground of the forest. It was a magnificent full set, abandoned due to the normal processes of nature, by a male red deer. For this cunning little fellow the antlers presented an opportunity to make a shilling or two by selling them to a local antique shop. Mounted on a polished mahogany base, they would look beautiful above the door of someone's house, so Claude Jeremiah promptly decided to take them home. He would clean them, and fix them to a suitable plaque, and sell them.

On the face of things it was a perfectly reasonable decision. The snag was that Claude Jeremiah Greengrass did not know the provisions of Section 2 of the Deer Act, 1963. This probably had little bearing on events because, if he had known, it would not have made the slightest difference to his actions. He would still have taken those antlers from the wood; he was that sort of villain. Acting in accordance with his instincts, therefore, he began to walk in triumph from the pine forest, proudly bearing aloft a particularly fine set of red deer antlers.

But even the best-laid plans go wrong: Claude Jeremiah had not bargained for the presence of Mr Archibald Flint. Mr Flint was a gamekeeper employed for the sole purpose of discouraging poachers and vandals. He was a dedicated keeper with some years' expertise and there were few men in the area who knew more about wild life and the host of laws which protect nature from poachers and their ilk. Flint was a genuine expert both in practice and in theory.

Having heard the twig-crackling approach of Claude Jeremiah Greengrass around one o'clock that morning Mr Flint sought refuge among the shadows of his hilltop kingdom. He was able to silently follow Claude Jeremiah about the woods and watch every move he made.

Because he was a stealthy man with many years of practice Mr Flint had followed the blissfully happy Claude Jeremiah for a considerable time before the latter had accidentally stumbled across the discarded antlers. It is interesting to speculate upon the thoughts ranging through Flint's skull as Claude Jeremiah's torch identified them as something special. And when Claude Jeremiah picked them from the ground Flint must have suffered chest pains. By 2.30 that morning Claude Jeremiah was leaving the woods with the antlers firmly in his possession. It was then that Archibald Flint pounced. He made threatening gestures with his twelve-bore shotgun and encouraged Claude Jeremiah to walk in front of it to a small gamekeeper's hut on the edge of the forest.

It was soon after this stage that I entered the story. Mr Flint telephoned our Divisional Office to announce his success and I was dispatched in the little Ford car to rendezvous with Flint and Greengrass in the isolated hut.

An oil lamp was burning because someone had stolen the electric bulb, and I found Mr Flint sitting at one side of the rough wooden table with Claude Jeremiah sitting at the other. His brown, leathery face was wrinkled in disgust as the sombre gamekeeper maintained his vigil with the gun pointing directly at him across the table. The antlers in dispute rested on the table.

I entered breezily and said, "Well, Mr Flint, what is it this time?"

Flint poured out the story of his careful surveillance of the prowling poacher and during this account Claude Jeremiah sat motionless and speechless. He had been to court enough times to know that any interruption was futile. It was far better to hear out the opposition because he'd then know the strengths and weaknesses of the other's story. He would get his opportunity to deliver a speech in due course.

I listened as the gamekeeper spoke in short, clipped phrases as if giving evidence in court, but I did not make any comment. I just gathered facts. I lifted the antlers, examined them and said, "Well, Claude Jeremiah?"

"There's nothing wrong in helping myself to a set of antlers, Mr Rhea, is there? They was lying on the ground. Like a lump of wood. I didn't poach the deer they belonged to, did I? He knows I didn't. It was just the antlers."

"He didn't kill the deer, did he?" I asked Flint.

"He did not," said Flint emphatically. "He took antlers. Antlers are part of a deer. It's in the Deer Act, Constable. It is an offence to take deer."

"I did not take deer, Mr Rhea," cried Claude Jeremiah, and I must admit I felt sorry for him. If I'd found his handsome set during one of my patrols, I might have been tempted to keep them.

"Is it alleged that he took a deer?" I put to Flint.

"Deer and part of deer are the same; Section 9. By taking part of a deer he's committing an offence which is equal to taking a whole deer. Antlers are part of a deer, Constable."

"Show me."

The gamekeeper sighed and produced a small handbook from his interior pocket. He flipped it open at the relevant page. I peered at it in the flickering light and saw the vital words.

"He's right," I said to Claude Jeremiah. "It means court for you."

"I'll be a witness," volunteered Flint.

I knew of no power to arrest Claude Jeremiah for this offence, therefore I made a note of his personal particulars, which I knew by heart anyway. I cautioned him in the traditional way by telling him he was not obliged to say anything, but whatever he did say would be taken down in writing and may be given in evidence. I concluded by saying he would be reported for taking a deer at night contrary to the Deer Act, 1963.

"I just took the antlers, that's all," was his reply, which I noted.

I let him go but retained the antlers for evidence. I told Mr Flint that he would be informed of the court date in due course and that Claude Jeremiah would receive a summons. The formalities over, I gave Claude Jeremiah a lift back into Aidensfield and dropped him near his home. During that short trip he expressed his hatred of gamekeepers in general, and Archibald Flint in particular, but refused to tell me why he'd been prowling around Brock Rigg forest during the night. After our chat I resumed my patrol.

In Eltering police office I entered the saga in my notebook and checked with *Stone's Justices Manual* on the veracity of Flint's claim. That reference book appeared to support his belief that antlers were classified as entire deer and I found no previously decided cases which might counter this. In short, it would be for our local court to determine this important issue.

Within a few days I had typed my account of the incident and had obtained a long written statement from Archibald Flint. He compiled his statement as a policeman would and appeared overjoyed at actually catching this notorious local poacher red-handed. I've no doubt that Claude Jeremiah had been in those woods on many previous occasions without being caught, so perhaps this was justice of a kind. But we were not judging previous occurrences, and I submitted my report through Sergeant Blaketon, who agreed with everything Flint said and informed me he would recommend prosecution.

At first I did wonder if a written caution might have been appropriate rather than a hearing in court, but later agreed with Blaketon's decision. With a man like Flint pushing for a conviction it was best to let Eltering Magistrates' Court decide the issue. The matter would thus receive a public hearing.

In due course summonses were issued and the participants instructed to be at Eltering Magistrates' Court at 10.30 am one Thursday morning. Alderman Fazakerly was Chairman and his accompanying magistrates were Mrs Pinkerton and Mr Smithers, with the efficient Mr Whimp as clerk of the court. The hearing opened with the usual applications for extensions of hours at local pubs and our case was first on the agenda.

"Claude Jeremiah Greengrass," called the usher, and the untidy figure of my beat's most notorious criminal shuffled forward and stood before the assembled Bench.

"Is your name Claude Jeremiah Greengrass?" asked Mr Whimp.

"Aye, it is," smiled Claude Jeremiah having answered this question in this court many times before.

"Listen carefully as I read out the charge. When I have finished you may plead either guilty or not guilty. Is that understood?" Greengrass nodded.

"Claude Jeremiah Greengrass. You are charged that, on Friday, 27th September last, you took a deer during the night — that is between the expiration of the first hour after sunset and the commencement of the last hour before sunrise, contrary to Section 2 of the Deer Act, 1963. How do you plead?"

"I didn't, sir. All I took was a pair of cast antlers, honest."

"Am I right in thinking it is your intention to plead not guilty?"

"Yes, sir, I'm not guilty. I didn't take a deer, Your Worships, I found a set of antlers, old ones they were. That's all."

"Thank you. You will get an opportunity to address the court. In the meantime you may sit down until it is your turn to give evidence. The offence with which you are charged is a summary offence and must be dealt with by this court."

Mr Whimp sat down with a flourish typical of magistrates' clerks everywhere as Sergeant Blaketon rose to address their Worships. He was a fine figure of a man, standing in this rural centre of justice as he outlined the facts of the case. He summarised the evidence which would be given by Archibald Flint and called the gamekeeper to the witness box. Flint gave a textbook account of the incident and concluded by producing Exhibit "A", the antlers, duly labelled.

Next was an expert witness from the Forestry Commission, a Mr FNZ Carruthers who told the court that the antlers were those of the red deer *(Cervus elaphus scoticus),* a species which frequented the plantation, although rare in other parts of England. It was plentiful in Scotland.

I was then called to give my evidence. I had to tell the court that, acting upon information received, I proceeded to Brock Rigg Plantation where I saw the accused and a set of antlers. I told the court of my brief interview, my cautioning of the defendant and his replies. I told of my seizure of evidence which I had labelled Exhibit 'A' and now produced.

When Mr Whimp asked Claude Jeremiah if he wanted to ask me any questions he leapt up and asked, "Did I have a deer with me, Mr Rhea?"

"No, Your Worships," I said. "Just a set of antlers."

"So I didn't take a deer," and he sat down in triumph.

There being no further prosecution witnesses and no defence witnesses, next in the box was Claude Jeremiah Greengrass. He elected to give evidence from the witness box and solemnly took the oath before beginning his account.

"I've always wanted a set of antlers, sir, to hang on my wall. I knew they'd put red deer in those woods to see if they would breed. You don't get many red deer in England, sir, do you? Scotland, yes, but not England. Anyway, I went up that night for a look around, just in case there was some lying discarded, you understand. The bucks discard their antlers, you see, knock 'em off on tree branches. Well, I found yon set, nice pair they are too. Just lying on the ground. So I picked 'em up and got to the edge of the wood when Flint caught me. I didn't kill the deer to get them antlers, honest. They was just lying there."

No one wished to put any questions to Claude Jeremiah Greengrass because the facts were not in dispute, and he was allowed to stand down. Alderman Fazakerly leaned from his lofty seat and whispered to Mr Whimp. I heard the loud whisper.

"I fail to see the point of this case," he said. "The fellow has obviously not killed or taken a deer, even if it was at night."

"No, sir," advised the patient Mr Whimp. "That is not the allegation."

"Isn't it? Then what is?"

"The case is based on the definition of a deer, sir."

"Oh," blinked Alderman Fazakerly. "Is the prosecution trying to say that a set of antlers is a deer?"

"That would appear to be the interpretation, Your Worships," smiled Mr Whimp. "The relevant authority is in the Deer Act, section 9," and he handed up a copy of *Stone's Justices Manual,* open at the correct page. I knew what it said, for I had read it some days ago. It stated that for the purposes of the Deer Act, 'a *deer means deer of any species and includes the carcass of any deer or any part thereof.*'

"The antlers are not a carcass, are they?" simpered Mrs Pinkerton.

"No, but they are part of one," grunted Mr Smithers. "And they are part of a deer. The Act says that part of a deer is a deer."

"It seems a bit hard on the fellow, doesn't it?" the Chairman whispered. "It's not as if he's been poaching red deer, is it?"

"The Act says it is illegal to take deer at night," Smithers spoke bluntly. "He's admitted that, so he's guilty. Part of a deer is the same as a whole deer. The law says so."

"Mrs Pinkerton?" asked the Chairman.

"The law is the law, so I must agree," she simpered.

"Thank you," the Chairman smiled. "I also agree. He's guilty. What about a penalty?"

The advisory Mr Whimp came to the rescue. "The offence carries a maximum fine of £20 for a first conviction," he said smugly.

Fazakerly pursed his lips. "I'd prefer an absolute discharge on this occasion. As you are aware, that is legally a penalty and a conviction, although it carries no fine or other sanction."

They all agreed, so Alderman Fazakerly raised his head and addressed the assembled court, including Claude Jeremiah Greengrass.

"Claude Jeremiah Greengrass," he cleared his throat in a judicial manner. "The Deer Act was created to protect these beautiful creatures from poachers, and Parliament has seen fit to regard parts of a deer as equivalent to the complete animal. Because you have admitted taking antlers at night you are therefore guilty of the offence as charged."

"Never!" cried the defendant.

"Is anything known against the accused?" Alderman Fazakerly asked Sergeant Blaketon.

Blaketon read out a list of his previous convictions, petty as they all were.

"Hm. Nothing serious, and no previous deer-poaching, eh? Well, Mr Greengrass, on this occasion we are prepared to grant you an absolute discharge. This means that, although you have been found guilty, there will be no penalty and no conditions as to your future conduct."

"That's very kind of you, sir, very kind indeed," and the relief was clear in his voice.

Sergeant Blaketon jumped to his feet.

"Would Your Worships care to make an order for the disposal of Exhibit 'A'?"

"Ah, of course. Well, as it was clearly found on Forestry Commission land, it must belong to them. The court therefore orders that the antlers be restored to the Forestry Commission. Perhaps Mr Carruthers will accept them?"

Carruthers smiled. "In the event of a penalty other than a fine, Your Worships, I am authorised to donate them to the defendant, as a gift."

"Then let it be done," smiled Alderman Fazakerly.

And the weathered face of Claude Jeremiah Greengrass broke into a cheeky smile. Flint, on the other hand, turned a deep purple, and failed to appreciate this court's administration of rural justice.

Poachers are an integral part of village life. They are not all of Claude Jeremiah's calibre, although a rural beat like Aidensfield certainly possesses its share of grouse-grabbing villains. Most are local folks, men whose ancestors have been poachers over countless generations and for whom poaching is a natural pastime like walking or breathing. Coping with them is never difficult because the gamekeepers know them and know how to deal with them, albeit unofficially at times. For the gamekeeper and the local poacher the eternal contest is almost like a game — sometimes you win, sometimes you lose. In many cases a friendly rivalry exists, although it can be a serious contest at times.

Part of the reason for the cosy attitude is that the poaching laws are so mysterious to those who do not understand their requirements. They create offences which are not theft, but which involve trespass. There are many offences within the scope of the poaching laws, and the illegality is created when poachers *trespass* in pursuit of game. The actual taking of game cannot be theft because the creatures are wild by nature, consequently it is trespass which forms the basis of the offences.

This makes it fun for the poacher. The sport can be compared with schoolboys sneaking into gardens to steal apples, although it must be said that there is big money in poaching and that pinching apples from gardens *is* theft!

It is the likelihood of big money that attracts carloads of highly skilled and ruthless poachers from the cities. These are the real villains, and they are a far cry from the village poacher who takes the occasional pheasant or salmon for his family lunch. These rogues journey into the rural regions of Yorkshire, there to give the estates a 'bashing', as they term it. They've even been known to use explosives to stun fish in rivers in order to collect them in large quantities, while some of the cunning methods used to catch game-birds are fascinating. For example, raisins are sometimes soaked in brandy and this gets pheasants so drunk they cannot fly off. A drunk and disorderly pheasant is a curious sight.

My beat was attractive to poachers because it was the location of several large country estates. Some possessed the traditional lord of the manor and a large mansion for him to live in. These people were good to me and were good to the local residents, consequently none of us disliked people of quality. In fact, they were good for the district because they provided work for the communities and therefore helped preserve village life. Their extinction will be a tragedy for England.

For the poachers of industrial West Yorkshire, however, the presence of such happy hunting-grounds within an hour's drive of their back-to-back homes or high-rise flats was very tempting and challenging. There were reports of luscious pheasants, succulent partridges, juicy salmon and other culinary delights, all waiting to be taken by skilful and daring men, and quite free of charge too. All that was needed was a little time and patience. One of my regular and important duties was to liaise with gamekeepers and keep their lordships informed of trends and poaching intelligence. Like all country policemen I reckoned it would be nice to arrest an organised bunch of poachers.

An opportunity to do that arose one autumn evening. I was on night-duty and had elected to patrol the village on foot, for it was a Saturday. On that night especially, the local people liked to pop out to the pub for a noggin or two. I entered the Brewers Arms at Aidensfield shortly before 10.30 to pay my customary uniformed visit. I knew the appearance of a uniformed bobby was appreciated by most landlords who wanted rid of hangers-on and who liked to go to bed at the same time as everyone else. I poked my head around the door to let everyone know I was about. The place was full; there was noise, laughter, happiness and music and there seemed to be no juvenile boozers or troublesome characters.

I waved across the sea of heads at the landlord, who saw me and waved back. Word would get about that the law was prowling and the drinkers would go peacefully to their homes. One or two locals made jokes about my presence and I was preparing to leave when the landlord hailed me.

He didn't shout for me; he just raised his hand and I recognised the signal. He wanted help or advice. This pre-arranged signal did not attract attention, so I went outside to wait. He followed and joined me soon afterwards, panting slightly.

"Glad I caught you," he said. "Did you notice those men in the corner?"

I shook my head. The place had been packed and, besides, not all the regular patrons were known to me.

"Strangers," he said. "I don't know them, but Sam over-head them talking."

"Go on, George," he was also called George, like the landlord of the Hopbind Inn at Elsinby. I wondered if all landlords were known as George.

"They were talking of giving his Lordship's river a bashing tonight," he told me. "Sam definitely heard them. Salmon, you know."

"Thanks," I valued this information. "Has the river been done before?"

"Once or twice, down at Victoria's Bend."

"Victoria's Bend?" I didn't know it.

"Halfway between here and Ploatby. It's a wide, sweeping bend in the river, and I'm told there's salmon in there, lots of them. It's named after Queen Victoria — she used to come and stay at the Hall and liked to sit down there near the river in the summer. It's been called Victoria's Bend ever since."

"I know it now," I recognised it from his description. "Right, thanks George. I'll inform the keeper."

"He's in hospital, broken ankle," George said.

I cursed under my breath. I'd have to cope myself for I was the only policeman on night-duty, although Sergeant Bairstow was on patrol elsewhere in the Sub-Division. I peered at the two suspicious men through a side window, so I'd know them again, then rang the sergeant from my own office. He was out and his wife did not know where he was, but she did inform me that he was expected back about one o'clock in the morning. He was obviously supervising several night-duty constables.

I decided to visit the location of the anticipated bashing in order to familiarise myself with the layout of the ground, river and trees. I walked along the rocky path which followed the line of the bubbling water and came to the long, sweeping curve in question. I knew this to be the haunt of succulent salmon and, wondering about their habits and movements, I spent some minutes there, trying to work out the likely movements of the poachers.

In order to catch them I would have to wait in hiding until they proved the purpose of their visit by lowering lines or nets into the water. Those actions alone would be proof of their intent and I could give such evidence in court. But I had to see them do it. I found a convenient clump of bushes about fifteen yards from the river bank and concealed myself behind it. From here I had a clear view up river towards the direction from which the anticipated poachers would come. I looked at my watch.

It was just after eleven o'clock.

I waited for about an hour and a half and began to wonder if my time was being wasted. Maybe we'd panicked? Maybe it was a joke between the two men? I thought of all the other things I could be usefully doing, like drinking tea in friendly houses or shaking hands with yet more doorknobs in Ashfordly. Maybe the pub had done this to get me out of the way so they could drink late? All manner of thoughts, nice and nasty, passed through my mind as I waited among the shrubbery and then I became aware of the approach of two men.

They walked very quietly, using the same path I had walked along. Even in the gloom I could see they carried rods, nets and gaffs, and wore waders. They were well equipped for their mission. As they neared me, I could hear them whispering softly and soon they found a small promontory about fifty yards beyond me. They settled upon this, rigged up their rods, nets and gaffs and prepared for their vigil. I watched them all the time, making notes of the precise time and their actions. I waited. It would be nice to catch them red-handed with a salmon — that would be perfect proof. Should I wait for that? Or pounce now? I had enough proof to justify action.

Suddenly the water broke violently and there developed a fierce thrashing and lots of vile cursing; they'd got one, a big one, judging by the fight it was creating. The water turned white about their feet as they gradually hauled the catch towards the shore. I saw the glint of the cruel gaff as it embedded itself into the flesh of the fish. Still thrashing wildly the gleaming fish was lifted bodily from the water and cast deftly on to the bank where the men pounced upon it. It would be swiftly killed.

As they worked on their prize I crept from my hiding place and was upon them before they realised I was there. I said all the proper things about being caught poaching, cautioned them officially and "seized" their lines, rods, gaffs and nets, plus the salmon. That was my evidence. I had half expected them to make a run for it, but they didn't. They accepted their arrest most peacefully and I marched them back to the village and up the hill to my police house. They made no excuse and never attempted to escape from me. I was thankful, if surprised, at their meek submission.

I rang Sergeant Bairstow because he would have to officiate in the office as they were charged. He was now at home, it being half past one in the morning, and I passed on my glad tidings. He grumbled and cursed because I'd got him out of bed, but I chose to ignore his feelings as I prepared to drive my prisoners into his office. He would charge and bail them.

In the car the two poachers remained silent and I found it most surprising that these men were models of good behaviour. I'd heard of poachers attacking bailiffs, gamekeepers and policemen while in the act of making arrests, and I'd also heard of poachers running into the darkness never to be seen again. But these characters never spoke a word in anger and never gave me a minute's trouble.

They provided their names and addresses. Both lived in York and seemed quite blasé about us keeping their expensive tackle. Charlie Bairstow bailed out each man in the sum of £25 to appear at Eltering Magistrates' Court in two weeks' time to answer several poaching charges. They hadn't a licence to fish for salmon or trout and were to be summoned for several fishery offences. All these were listed, and the police would act as agents for the Fishery Board because there were offences involving their activities on private land.

At the conclusion of the formalities the men apologised profusely for their actions and left the office. I remained behind to provide a quick account for Sergeant Bairstow and he listened intently.

"Nice work, Nicholas," he smiled. "You've made a couple of good arrests there. Night poaching, eh? The magistrates will love this one."

"Thanks, Sergeant."

"Now you'd better go and get the others."

"Others?"

"Yes, others, Nicholas. There will be others, probably several of them."

"There was only that couple, Sergeant."

"That's right. They would be the advance party, sent deliberately to get caught. Think about it, Nicholas. Think about tonight's events. Those men enter a local pub where strangers are immediately recognised, and they begin talking about giving his Lordship's river a bashing. Why do that? Why tell the locals what they're up to? You are told, and you lie in wait — they turn up laden to the eyeballs with fishing gear and you arrest them. A good job, well done. But it's all too easy, Nicholas. Did you notice how they left this office? They didn't ask for a lift anywhere, did they? I'm bloody sure their car isn't in Ashfordly, not when they were drinking in Aidensfield pub. Someone would be waiting for them. Now they'll all go back to Victoria's Bend and give those salmon a real bashing. The money they'll make tonight will pay the fines of the two volunteers and everyone will be happy — except his Lordship."

I considered his theory. It seemed feasible and I must admit that I had been surprised by the submissive attitude of the two poachers. I thought it all over right from the start and reckoned Charlie Bairstow was right.

"I'll go back and arrest the others, Sergeant."

"Not on your own, you won't. This needs more of us — the next lot won't be as gentlemanly as your first catch."

"There's only you and I," I said.

"Then I'll organise help," he assured me. "I can rustle up a constable from Eltering, and I believe the dog section is on patrol in Malton. They've been to a late-night dance — they can be here in half-an-hour."

"Shall I go and keep observations?" I asked.

He shook his head.

"No, think it through, Nicholas. What is going through *their* minds right now?"

"They'll be waiting until the coast is clear," I said.

"And is it clear? If you were a villain, doing what I believe they're doing, would you consider the coast to be clear?"

"No, not until the bobby has gone to bed."

"Exactly. They'll be waiting for you to turn in."

"I'm on nights," I said.

"They won't know that. There's no reason why you shouldn't *pretend* to go to bed, is there?"

"Ah!" I got the gist of his thinking, then realised my pretended return for bed would arouse Mary and the children.

"Right," he said. "Go home. Park your motorbike in the garage and go into the house. Go through all the motions of going to bed — lights on downstairs, office light on. Office light off, kitchen light on as if you're having a cup of coffee. Bathroom and bedroom lights. OK?"

"Yes, Sergeant."

"Then when the house is in darkness creep out and make sure no lights are on. Meet me at 2.30 behind the Brewers Arms, on foot. Wait there until I arrive with reinforcements."

"Yes, Sergeant."

"I'm sorry if it disturbs your family, but it's a worthwhile job."

I left Ashfordly police office on my motorcycle and chugged noisily home. I hoped my furtive activities would not cause too much upset among my family, but they were accustomed to the strange comings and goings of my motorcycle. I placed the machine inside the garage and went through the routine of booking off duty and going to bed. Inside the house I switched on the kitchen light as I walked through to the office and switched on the kettle for a coffee. In the office I sat at my desk to write up my notebook as I would have done. Then I switched off the office light, adjourned to the kitchen and brewed myself a drink. I took it into the living room, making sure all the lights were on, and I enjoyed the brief rest. Upstairs there was not a sound. I hadn't wakened them.

Having enjoyed the drink I pretended to climb the stairs to bed. Lights went off and on as I went about my fictitious movements, but there was not a murmur from the family. It made me realise how easy it is to burgle a house . . .

Once all this performance was over I crept out of the house, which I left in total darkness, and made my way on foot down to the village. It was about 2.20 and there was not a soul about. I crept into the pub carpark and was greeted by the rapid flash of a torch. Sergeant Bairstow had arrived.

"Okay?" he asked.

"Fine," I said. "And not a murmur from the kids."

"Good, let's go. Is there an approach for us that isn't direct from here?"

"We can go through Home Farm fields," I told him.

"Lead on," and I realised he had an army of policemen with him. Two men whose names I did not know were in the shadows, each with a police dog and there was another tall, senior police constable whom I guessed was from Malton.

We marched through the darkness with me leading the way. We did not speak as I led them through a small copse and into the fields of Home Farm. We kept close to the hedges, which provided shelter, and after twenty minutes I halted them.

"The river is down there," I said, pointing to the brow of a small hillock. "Behind that hill the bank goes fairly steeply towards the river. The banks are lined with bushes and trees. The curve known as Victoria's Bend is down there — that's the favourite place for salmon."

"I don't know what to expect," said Bairstow. "I don't know how many we'll find — if any! I imagine there'll be those we nicked earlier and their mates. Maybe two carloads. Seven or eight of 'em," and he outlined a plan of action. We would use our torches or police whistles as signals.

"The dogs can cope," said one of their handlers, when I expressed concern that the poachers might be armed.

"We'll use one dog at each side of them," said Bairstow. "And one of us at each side too. I'll stay with Nick — he knows the lie of the land."

Two constables, one of whom was a dog handler with his Alsatian straining at the leash, vanished to my right and were quickly lost in the shadows. They moved silently across the turf, climbed the fence and were soon moving through the woodland towards the river bank on my right. Bairstow, the other dog handler and I crossed the fence to our left and clambered down the hillside. I felt we were making far too much noise, but Bairstow didn't call for silence.

Soon Sergeant Bairstow halted and pointed.

"There!" he whispered, and I followed the line of his outstretched arm.

Silhouetted against the silvery sheen of the moving water were several heads, all working at the river's edge. I could hear the roar of the rapids higher upstream and realised this noise would conceal our movements. I counted five men. I guessed there would be more, the others perhaps posted as look-outs.

We were below the skyline and, as we neared the water's edge, the woodland thinned considerably. Finally we reached the riverside path. Bairstow waited for several long, agonising minutes and then flashed his torch twice, very quickly. The response came immediately — two flashes. The others were in a similar position, ready for action.

We moved forward, knowing our colleagues at the other side were doing likewise, closing in and making a sandwich of the poachers. Then up went a warning shout. It surprised us all. We'd been seen.

"Bailiffs!"

A man had been concealed behind a bush on the river bank and we almost tripped over him. Too late we realised he was there. He ran from us, shouting his warning as he rushed towards his pals.

Sergeant Bairstow did not flap. He simply stood his ground, pulled out his police whistle and blew it. It was the first time I'd heard a police whistle used on duty, and it galvanised us into action. The dogs were told to "speak" and began to bark as Sergeant Bairstow called upon the poachers to stand still or be bitten in some very painful places. Four of them stood rock still, but one tried to escape by climbing over a fence into the fields beyond.

The look-out had vanished too, but a dog handler now called to them all, albeit addressing the man heading for the railings.

"Halt or the dog comes after you!" he bellowed. The running man did not halt. He ran for all he was worth, and I heard the handler tell his dog to deal with the escapee. He slipped the lead and with a glorious bound the agile dog leapt in pursuit of the frantic man. The other dog barked encouragement from the distance and it seemed as if this character was the only one foolish enough to attempt to outrun the dogs. Its handler followed with fitful strides as the bounding dog pursued the foolish poacher.

He could never hope to outdistance the dog, but someone must have given wings to the fellow's heels for he did manage to clamber over the fence and was precariously balanced on top when the dog arrived. In the dim light we could see the drama. The man was balanced on top of the railings and was preparing to leap down into the field. At the precise moment he took off, the dog leapt up and seized his arm. With a cry of horror the man fell, and we heard the tell-tale growling and snarling of a police dog which had cornered its prey.

"Leave!" cried the handler, and the dog sat back on its haunches, tongue lolling as it watched the sobbing, terrified youth. The others in the meantime, including the look-out man, had been gathered into a huddle and were guarded by the other dog. Its presence was enough to guarantee their cooperation.

The attempted escaper, who had fallen head first into a bunch of nettles, was gathered up and brought back.

We seized their gear for evidence, took them all to Ashfordly Police Station and bailed them out to appear before Eltering Magistrates' Court in due course. It was a skilful gang from Leeds, but the pair we'd caught earlier were not among them. None of this gang admitted knowing the other two, but I didn't believe them.

From our point of view it had been a good night's work, and I collapsed into bed at 6.30, tired but happy after the night's events. I told myself that when I woke around lunchtime I would ring his Lordship to acquaint him with our overnight success. He'd be pleased, I knew; maybe we'd each receive a complimentary salmon!

But his Lordship woke me at 8.30 by banging on the door of the house and demanding to see me. Mary had to arouse me, due to his insistence, and I staggered bleary-eyed downstairs to find him in the lounge, flustered and angry. Very angry indeed.

"Poachers!" he shouted. "I had poachers last night, Rhea! Down at Ferris Bridge. They've given me a right bashing and here's you, lying in bed all day . . ."

I groaned.

CHAPTER SIX

His motorcar was poetry and tragedy,
love and heroism. The office was his pirate ship,
but the car his perilous excursion ashore.
SINCLAIR LEWIS — *Babbitt*

In my early days in the police force it was considered by those
in authority that motorcars were not for ordinary policemen,
either at work or at play. That a constable could or would
even own a car was something abhorrent and this thinking
was reflected in the fact that police houses had no garages,
police stations had no parking places and police training
centres issued "Guidance to Students on Arrival" without
once mentioning a motorcar. Perhaps Scotland Yard did not
subscribe to this image because old films about the police
invariably showed a long-snouted Wolseley roaring out of
the pearly gates of that famous Police Headquarters. Indeed,
many police forces later advertised Henry Ford's cars in
sombre black garb as they rushed up and down main roads
with "Police" written all over them. In those days "Police"
was synonymous with efficiency and quality, and I'm sure
the police forces who used Ford cars provided useful, albeit
unconscious, recommendation for Mr Ford's engineering

skills. Another peculiarity was that detective story writers rarely used motorcars in their yarns to convey detectives around, even though some of their detective inspectors did dress for dinner and take sherry in country houses.

The reality of police thinking suggested that a constable driving a car was akin to a gardener using his master's Rolls-Royce, so the perambulations around our beats meant we had to rely heavily upon our feet or else use very ancient pedal cycles. Cycles were unreliable because the lamps never worked, and the tyres were always flat. Official cycles were large, upright monsters, painted black all over and sporting a chain guard. For years they provided the traditional mode of transport for the travelling constable, and still do in some areas. The constable went to work upon it, did his work upon it and travelled home upon it. Some forces actually paid an allowance to those who used their own pedal cycles for duty, and as this was based on the mileage covered on duty, little books were issued to the riders in which the official mileage was recorded and checked carefully by the sergeant.

Eltering's official cycle was rusty and unfit for duty. The inspector requested a replacement; in fact, he was extremely daring because he applied for two country bicycles, basing his claim on the fact that the establishment of his officers had doubled since 1910 and new roads, coupled with expanding villages, had brought more people within range of our patrols. Much to his surprise his wish came true — the Police Committee at County Hall considered his application and allocated two new pedal cycles to Eltering Police Station. Sergeant Blaketon was appointed officer in charge of county cycles and promptly numbered them 1 and 2. He issued a mileage book to each machine. No 1 cycle was to be used as the main machine, with No 2 being used only in emergencies or when No 1 was otherwise engaged. After each journey the mileage book must be completed showing the date, times and places visited with the name of the rider in charge at the time. He further instructed that after use the cycles had to be checked for cuts in the tyres, damage or loss of wind;

the lights must be checked, and the saddle cleaned for use. In this manner, therefore, the constables of Eltering became mechanised.

It was some time before I understood why Eltering managed to acquire two cycles. A few years later I learned that the Police Committee had been considering the issue of motor-cars to selected town stations like Eltering. It transpired that the inspector had applied for two pedal cycles and had put up such a good argument for them that the Committee felt Eltering did not require a car. Ashfordly got a little car and so did Malton, while Eltering continued for years with pedal cycles.

A little Ford Anglia did arrive in due course, and indeed most rural stations eventually possessed one of these delightful vehicles. At the larger stations the Superintendent had a large Ford, usually a Consul, while the inspector made do with a Morris Oxford. No one else was allowed to use these sacred treasures and they were treated like pots of gold. The Superintendent's car was cleaned, oiled and maintained by a mechanically qualified constable, who also lit the fires, looked after stray dogs, cooked the meals for prisoners and did every other job around the station. He also spared a moment for the inspector's car, but studiously refrained from interfering with the pedal cycles. Another less talented officer cared for these machines.

It goes without saying that it was never easy travelling from place to place during routine duties. If our cycles lacked the speed necessary to reach emergencies while they were still emergencies we had to improvise and we did this by standing in the middle of the road in full uniform with hand raised. This was guaranteed to stop most vehicles and in this grand manner we begged or bullied lifts, or we took a bus.

Under no circumstances must we use either the inspector's or the Superintendent's car. Even though they were official vehicles, it was understood they were official only to those exalted ranks and were most definitely not for the likes of working constables rushing off to deal with burglaries, rapes, sudden deaths or mayhem of other kinds. They were used to convey the higher ranks to their dinners and other important social functions.

There were occasions, however, when ambitious constables let their crime-detecting ardour get the better of them to such an extent that they made use of the Superintendent's car. The horror of such an action was too fearful to contemplate, but this happened to me on one occasion.

I was working "office nights" at Divisional Headquarters during a shortage of men, and the time would be around two o'clock in the morning. The telephone rang, a rare event in that station at any time, but particularly so at this early hour. I answered it. A very anxious gentleman was calling from a kiosk in the marketplace and his message was to the effect that his car had just been stolen and was, at this very moment, being driven out of town at the hands of an unscrupulous villain. The gentleman provided the registration number and a brief description of his vehicle, so I asked him to make his way to the office where a colleague would look after him. Meanwhile I would give chase. There was not a moment to lose.

I rang Control Room and provided them with a description, saying the stolen vehicle was heading towards York. Control Room promised assistance in the shape of a modern, highly sophisticated police patrol car. I could hardly set off in pursuit on my motorcycle — by the time I'd got myself dressed in my plethora of gear, the car would be miles away. I decided to use the Superintendent's car for it was parked in the station garage. I made this decision in the full realisation that my career might come to a sudden end, but villains are there to be caught. I might just catch this one. If I did nothing about it my career would come to a similarly swift end.

The gleaming car awaited. Its keys dangled from a hook in the Charge Office. Feeling almost as if I was taking this car without lawful consent, I took the keys and raced around to the garage. Within seconds I was on the road and enjoying the chase. There is little doubt that these official cars were beautifully maintained and tuned. The policemen who looked after them nursed a deep pride in their work, and all vehicles were in a superb condition. There was not a scratch on this car and its paintwork gleamed. Its engine purred like a contented cat and I found myself humming with sheer enjoyment as I sped through the sleeping town in pursuit of the stolen car. This was the life!

I switched on the radio, gave my call-sign to Control Room as I booked on the air, and smiled at the consternation of those listeners-in who would think that the Superintendent was not only out on patrol, but hotly pursuing a stolen car. Such is the effect of a personalised call-sign like Mike One Zero Papa. I listened to the commentary on the radio — a York constable was heading towards me, hoping to head off the vehicle, and it was a fair bet that one of us would halt the flight of HAT 101. That number was etched into my memory.

I sped along the fine surface of the main road with the wind whistling about the car as I drove to its limit. I touched 100 mph and the car remained as steady as a rock. I had been mobile for some ten minutes when I heard Control Room announce to all involved in the hunt for HAT 101 that a village petrol-pump owner had heard a noise and had seen the driver helping himself to a tankful of fuel. I knew the village. It was off the main road, so I turned off its long, straight carriageway and bore along the peaceful dark lanes. I urged the willing vehicle into the bends and along the straights at speeds which would have terrified me under normal circumstances. There was a maze of lanes here, but I knew I wasn't far from the village in question. The car could be in any of these lanes.

Quite suddenly I came up behind the stolen car. It seemed the thief had not realised he was being chased because he was pottering along at a fairly sedate 45 mph. I was now faced with the problem of stopping him. This was not easy, especially on such narrow lanes, and it was before the days of blue revolving lights and flashing police signs. I had to rely on my headlight dip switch, horn and my voice. There was no loud hailer fitted to this car — some of the more splendid patrol cars possessed loud hailers from which booming voices, amplified many times, could halt a thief in seconds and arouse half the town in the process. But I had none of this sophisticated equipment, so I shouted out of the window, blared my horn and flashed my lights. It had some effect.

The driver thought I wanted to overtake him, so he pulled into the side of the lane to allow me through. At that stage, it seems, he realised it was a black car with no markings but containing a chap in uniform bent on stopping him. Quite understandably, he accelerated. I did likewise. Suddenly we were roaring alarmingly along the narrow lanes with lights flashing and horns blaring. Tall, thick hedges rushed at us on the corners and hills yawned before our noses. Houses tore past, and cattle shook their heads in bewilderment. How long we careered like this I do not know, but it seemed like hours. Then very unexpectedly he turned sharp left, which meant I had to brake urgently. Tyres screamed as I attempted his sudden change of direction and I found he had careered through an open farm gate and was currently sinking into a foul-smelling pond. I stopped at the edge as he clambered across the roof of the car, now up to his axles in slime, and I said, "Come on, you're under arrest."

"Oh, bloody hell!" he said in evident resignation and he came quietly as arrested persons tended to do in those halcyon days. I conveyed him to the police station where a sergeant now waited. The formalities of searching him, questioning him and eventually charging him were completed and the perplexed owner was taken out to retrieve his car from the pond. We drove the Superintendent's car on that trip too and used a tow-rope to haul the abandoned vehicle from its soggy parking place.

By six that morning the excitement was over. The man had been charged and would appear at court that morning. Meanwhile he would remain in the cells as a guest. The loser had got his car back, the farmer into whose pond the stolen car had dropped would have a tale to tell at market and I would be roused from my sleep by nine o'clock, only three hours later, in order to attend court and give my evidence. In those days policemen weren't supposed to need sleep.

I attended court and the case was rapidly dealt with, the thief pleading guilty to the offence of taking and driving away a car without the consent of the owner. He also pleaded guilty to careless driving and using the car without insurance. I gave evidence in the formal manner drummed into us at Training School and he got away with a total fine of £65 and had his licence endorsed.

I was then ordered into the inner sanctum, wherein dwelt the Superintendent. I expected praise for my part in effecting the swift arrest of the car thief but instead found myself facing a very red-faced and irate Superintendent who waved an official logbook at me. It belonged to his car.

"This!" he simmered. "This book — last night you drove over 100 miles in my official car — my car. Two trips, each of fifty . . ."

"Yes, sir," I said.

"But this is the *Superintendent's* car!" he bellowed. "It is not to be used for routine patrolling, not under any circumstances and certainly not by a constable."

"I was chasing a stolen car, sir," I began to explain. "I had no other means of catching the thief," and went into a long-winded and fairly exaggerated account of my escapade.

He fumed and panted as I continued, but my reasons were totally invalid. I almost felt he was going to charge me with taking and driving his car without consent! He told me again that Superintendent's official cars were not to be used for routine police work, they were for supervisory duties. In short, I got the bulling of my life and retracted from the office with my pride wounded. There was no doubt in my mind that if I had not used the Superintendent's car that thief would have escaped. I was convinced my actions were justified.

Higher authority didn't think so. My actions that night led to a Divisional Order which stated quite categorically that the Superintendent's official car must never be used for routine police patrol duties. It was a supervisory officer's vehicle for use by supervisory officers on supervisory duties.

Like all such orders, however, there was an escape clause. This allowed the car to be used for emergencies, but this permission was qualified by saying it could be done only by the personal consent of the Superintendent.

The inevitable happened. I was on night-duty some weeks later in the same police station when an almost identical event occurred. A householder heard noises in the street and looked out of the bedroom window in time to see his Morris Minor vanishing from sight. He immediately rang the police station and I answered the telephone; the result was a repeat performance of the previous escapade, except that I rang the Superintendent at home to get his personal permission to use his car.

Three o'clock in the morning is never a good time to arouse anyone from sleep, let alone one's superior officer, but he was very good about it. He said I could use his precious car to chase the thief. Actually, he had no alternative — to have refused would have created all manner of problems if I had had to explain to an even higher-ranking officer how I had been refused permission for operational reasons. So the chase began.

This crafty character selected a winding route which twisted through many villages. I knew it well, even though it was pitch black and even if I was perhaps a little more tired than I should be. But I knew the roads this thief was using, and, like the previous case, I guessed he would not realise he was being followed by a keen young constable.

I pressed the accelerator and the finely tuned car responded. It took me into those bends and along those roads with a whirr of tyres and a flash of speeding hedges, villages and lanes. I was enjoying myself, this was great. It was better than watching Edgar Lustgarten's films or re-enacting a

Scotland Yard chase in a Jaguar or something equally splendid. I was thrilling myself as I hurtled along those roads in the Superintendent's lovely vehicle.

Everything went well until I ran off the road. I still cannot remember where the road went, but I do recall sitting in the car and leaning forward at an alarming angle. The front wheels were in a ditch and the rear ones were spinning uselessly in mid-air. I switched off the engine, disengaged the gears and clambered out, dropping like a pilot from an aircraft as I landed on the grass verge beneath. The car smelled very hot and there were enough sods of grass lying about to carpet a cricket pitch.

I was totally alone. The place was deserted, and I had not arrested this thief. Luckily, the car radio still worked, so I called for assistance.

I had a very long and painful report to submit when I returned, and the Superintendent said he had no wish to see me.

I understand he was very upset about it.

Because policemen rarely owned vehicles they experienced great pleasure when sitting in the passenger seat of a shining black police patrol car. Riding in one of these gleaming machines was the next best thing to owning one, and the truth was that official motorcars remained a luxury in many forces even into the second half of the 20th century. Supervisory officers did use them but not constables on routine patrols.

It will be appreciated therefore that the opportunity to actually *drive* a powerful police car was considered one of the greatest possible honours. This honour was occasionally bestowed upon selected personnel who formed a specialised unit known as the Road Traffic Division.

Men selected for this duty were undoubtedly the *crème de la crème* of any police force. Not only had they proved themselves good practical police officers in the traditional style, but they had also shown themselves highly skilled in driving, even managing to retain their smartness in spite of the shiny seats of their trousers and the paunchy bellies which resulted from too many hours in the driving seat. These were the swashbuckling heroes, men with hair styles reminiscent of RAF officers during the war, always well-groomed and eye-catching. These were ladies' men, an elitist group with a penchant for obtaining cups of coffee in highway cafes and an ability to control a speeding car in all conditions. They were to the police service what fighter pilots were to the Royal Air Force.

They created legends in their own time. There were tales of skilled patrol car drivers waltzing their cars beautifully on ice, tales of high-speed drives across the moors to rescue suicidal men hanging by ropes from beams of ancient inns and daring chases to capture stolen vehicles or meet super-intendents at rendezvous points. Whatever they did became a talking point over coffee from our night-duty flasks; it was all thrilling stuff.

For the young policeman whose mode of conveyance was his feet this was a lifestyle to dream about. To become a patrol car driver was the ambition of many and the lot of a few. As if in answer to our dreams it was deemed by higher authority that all young constables should undergo a short attachment to Road Traffic Division.

This was to familiarise us with the miracles performed by this group of specialists so that we knew their abilities and capabilities. Thus in the course of our duties we could call upon their expertise, and it was hoped we would make greater use of these fine fellows in moments of stress or dire emergency. The cars used by these giants were different from ordinary police vehicles — they had radios for one thing, and their speedometers had been rigorously checked over a meas-ured mile in order that speeders could be safely prosecuted in court. These cars had signs right across the front which said POLICE, and which could be switched on at night. Their commodious boots were full of paraphernalia to deal with traffic accidents, like a broom for sweeping up broken glass and a shovel to put it on, a tape measure, cones for warning oncoming drivers, a first aid box, balls of string, lifting gear and a host of other useful things. Unlike modern police cars they did not have blue flashing lights, noisy horns and sneaky computers like VASCAR to trap speeders.

There is no doubt that these shining black cars held a certain enchantment and offered a romantic interlude in the average bobby's career. An attachment to Road Traffic Division, however short, must be considered a step towards this Valhalla. It so happened that my fortnight's attachment coincided with a period of night-duty, which meant I was allocated a night patrol in a warm police car. The arrangement was that I patrol my patch as usual, albeit in the company of a seasoned patrol driver, and our joint manoeuvres would satisfy his patrol requirements in addition to providing supervision of my beat during those nights. It seemed a reasonable compromise and I looked forward very much indeed to my introduction to Road Traffic Division's marvels and mysteries.

On the first evening I presented myself at Ashfordly Police Station where it had been arranged that my driver for the shift would collect me at 10.20. I was armed with a flask of coffee, tin of sandwiches and my trusty torch. At the appointed time my heavenly chariot arrived. It was a shining black Ford Consul known as Mike One Five, pronounced Mike One Fifer in phonetic jargon, and alternatively referred to as MI5. The car's unfortunate call-sign led it to being known as Mystery One Five or the Secret Service car and its driver was PC Rupert Langley.

He was a thirty-year-old married man with a lovely wife and two equally lovely children. Rupert and his family had transferred to the North Riding Constabulary from Kent because his wife loved horses and wide, open spaces. Malton, with its racing-stables and accessibility to the moors and dales, seemed a perfect posting although her love was for hunting and hacking rather than racing. None the less it was an ideal place for the Langley family to grow up.

Rupert was at least six feet two inches tall with a slim, athletic build topped by a mop of wavy black hair. The women he met a work and at play fell instantly in love with his dark, thoughtful eyes and it was said that many deliberately drove their cars carelessly or parked illegally in the hope he would take down their particulars. In spite of his suntanned magnetism he never strayed from his family home and was always faithful to his wife.

Few disliked Rupert, and I was delighted he was to show me the work of Road Traffic Division. He was highly articulate and very amusing, two talents that were quickly in evidence as he introduced himself and showed me around his car. It was clearly an object of pride for him as he explained how to operate the radio and how to use the various call-signs favoured by Road Traffic Division. He explained all about the speedometer, so accurate and tested regularly for evidential purposes, the specialist tools and equipment in the boot and finally the PA. I did not know much about the latter device, but studiously observed him as he operated a switch on the dashboard.

"That switches on the PA," he said, as if I knew all about it.

"Does it?" I wondered whether to show my ignorance, but he recognised my uncertainty.

"Public address system," he clarified the point. "About half our fleet is fitted with the public address system. It's a loud hailer device, really, worked off the battery. I just speak into the handset of the official radio," he picked up the handset "and switch it on. Then I can talk to crowds of people outside all at once or get cars to move aside or stop. Warn folks about lost drugs or bad road conditions. That sort of thing. It's marvellous. You can tell a whole street about a gas leak in no time."

To demonstrate it he switched on and said into the handset, "Good evening, friends." Outside the car his words boomed and echoed about the police station and I felt sure they would be heard as far away as the marketplace. I wondered what the townspeople would think as those words filled the night air and guessed a drunk or two might suddenly become sober.

Having seen the magic of the car I climbed in. I was now officially an "observer" and as such would be responsible for noticing offenders and incidents during this shift. I would also have to provide supporting evidence for any court case secured by Rupert.

Not knowing what excitements lay in store we set off smoothly, the beautifully tuned car transporting us in sheer luxury. We accelerated out of the police station yard and made for the tiny town centre. The official radio burbled quietly from the dashboard. It was my job to show Rupert around Ashfordly and district and I felt he was worthy of being shown some of our secret places, where tea and buns could be obtained at all hours. It was his task to educate me about the skills of his specialist department and our mutual task was to police the area tonight.

Rupert talked freely, and I found him easy and entertaining to listen to. As a southerner, he had found the North Riding people to be somewhat blunt at first but had since grown to like and respect them for their toughness and straight speaking. He had grown fond of the North Riding countryside too and talked of making it his permanent home. He liked his work, he was happy with his car and appreciated the opportunities provided for him. In short, he was happy; a rare and contented man.

Our first tour of duty was spent getting to know each other and attempting to understand each other's mode of working. Nothing of any great significance arose but our second shift was to prove much more interesting. We stopped one or two motorists to advise them about faulty lights, and I toured my vulnerable properties to check for signs of illegal entry. In this way we successfully combined our roles, and my beat remained peaceful.

Towards midnight we found ourselves in Brantsford marketplace and Rupert decided to park for a few minutes to observe the passing scene. This is always a useful exercise, although Brantsford dies at 10.30. That is the time the pubs close and, as that event had passed quietly, our vigil was distinctly lacking in action and pace. To be truthful, that was the situation until a stray dog appeared.

It was a cur dog, a type very common among the moorland farmers of this region. They are small, hardy animals, predominantly black with patches of white fur, and this one emerged from a side street to sniff the cool night air. It cocked its leg against a lamppost and wandered into the main street. It was quite alone.

I noticed Rupert lift the handset of his radio, but I did not link that action in any way with the dog. Next, he pressed he PA switch. This meant the public address system was alive.

That which followed was quite surprising. Rupert lifted the handset to his mouth and began to produce the most realistic sounds of a dogfight I've ever heard this side of Percy Edwards. The amplified battle cries reverberated across the town and it was as if all the hounds in hell were fighting in Brantsford High Street. The innocent cause of this commotion stood in the middle of the road, highlighted by a streetlamp with its hair standing on end, its tail as erect as a flagpole and its teeth bared in a realistic grimace as it sought its hidden foe. Rupert continued to growl and snarl until several doors opened and many lights came on; people came to see what was happening and one pub was cast open to discharge a late-night party into the street. Everyone wanted to observe the fight but all they found was a very puzzled cur dog alone in the middle of the street.

Then Rupert stopped.

It was amazing how busy the small town had become, and we now had something and somebody to watch. From the excited voices of the pub crowd it seemed they were members of a twenty-first birthday party which was being held for the landlord's daughter. The entire gathering from the pub was now in the street, all clutching glasses of drink and seeking nearby nooks and crannies for the dogfight. Up and down the street windows had opened both upstairs and downstairs, and curious folk leaned out, asking questions of one another and expressing their concern about uncontrolled dogs. The partygoers provided a backcloth of coarse humour for the roused residents, and among all this speculation and commotion the bewildered dog wandered about, now totally unconcerned about the flap it had caused.

Rupert sat with a big smile on his face and I laughed quietly at his side. It was almost like watching a live stage performance with no idea what was to follow.

"You've certainly livened up this place!" I chuckled. "It's quite busy now."

"It works wonders when things are quiet," he said, taking out his pipe and lighting it. "I find it fascinating to watch people as they hunt the dogfight. When they go in I'll do it again briefly. They'll all rush out again — they'll talk about it for ages afterwards."

And he did. Ten minutes later the cur had vanished and the drinkers had returned to their party. The windows had been closed, the doors had been locked and the town restored to its normal state of tranquillity. Rupert's second impression resulted in the ghastly amplified sound of dogs fighting to the death, two killers snarling their vengeance upon each other, howling and barking in the darkness.

From our vantage point we enjoyed a repeat performance as more lights came on, more doors opened, and the partygoers rushed out once again, laughing and shrieking as they nervously sought the Hound of the Baskervilles. By now my sides were aching with suppressed laughter but Rupert simply sat there, nursing his pipe as he observed the bewildered people trying to solve the mystery. I wondered what kind of rumours would be rife in the little town tomorrow and tried to visualise what Sergeant Blaketon would do when the tales reached his ears. He'd probably arrange a purge upon stray dogs.

"Let's take a walk," Rupert said quite suddenly, stuffing his pipe into the car's ashtray. We left the warmth and security of the car, walked into view of the people and patrolled the High Street much to the relief of the residents. Several asked if we'd heard the dogfight, and Rupert denied it. He explained that we'd just arrived, although he did mention a cur dog which was now trotting peacefully home along Junction Terrace. The final scene in this drama was an invitation to join the birthday festivities. We did this and enjoyed them tremendously. I could see that Rupert's talent was already paying dividends.

During the nights which followed I was to learn more of his unique and fascinating talent. In similar moments of inactivity I would ask him if he could mimic particular sounds and would challenge him with requests to copy things like squeaking gates or a roll of thunder. Invariably he could oblige.

Sometimes his art was undertaken in the privacy of the car without coming to the notice of the general public, but by far the most interesting sessions were those broadcast through the public address system of his patrol car.

I have seen women blush delightfully at a loud and sincere wolf-whistle coming from somewhere beyond their ken. I have seen those silly people about to jaywalk or drive their cars out of parking areas without looking, pull up sharply in the face of Rupert's stern warnings. I've known him bid "good morning" to his friends in this way and "goodnight" to home-going drunks. I've seen him remind his wife, whom he noticed out shopping, to bring home his favourite cheese or some meat for the cat. I've also watched him mischievously make totally unidentifiable sounds — one example is a simple clicking noise, the sort one does with one's mouth to encourage a horse to trot. When done through an amplifier in the street the noise can be very baffling and it's good fun to watch the genuine bewilderment on the faces of those who cannot identify it. Other small intriguing noises included clicking his fingernails into the mike, drumming his fingers on the side of the microphone, scraping a matchbox's sandpaper with a thumbnail or simply yawning loudly.

But it was his ability to imitate specific sounds which I found most interesting. He could produce an excellent cuckoo and I'm sure he was the cause of many rural folk writing to their newspaper to boast of hearing the season's first cuckoo. I have often wondered how many early cuckoos were Rupert idling his time in a layby. The blackbird's alarm call and the honk of a pheasant were nicely done too, and I'm sure he created despondency among the wildlife on my beat. I could imagine the local birds and beasts hearing these alarm calls and accepting them as genuine before scurrying to safety.

It is difficult to highlight the most memorable of his imitations but two remain etched in my memory. The first occurred in the very early hours of one morning when we had been diverted to the seaside town of Strensford upon a rather urgent enquiry. It was almost an hour's journey from our beat, but, as Rupert was the only patrol car driver on duty that night, it meant we had to undertake the task. We left Aidensfield at eleven to arrive about midnight and deal with the inquiry. It was no more than a traffic inquiry from a southern police force, but it demanded the knowledge of an expert Road Traffic officer because it involved the misuse of a Goods Vehicle Carrier's Licence. I didn't understand the urgency but went along and learned something of this branch of traffic law. We concluded at 1.30 and decided to have our meal break at Strensford.

We could have gone to the police station, but it was a lovely summer morning with a clear, bright sky, so we decided to enjoy our sandwiches and flasks on the cliff top. There we could enjoy the superb views out to sea and watch the coasters sailing by. Rupert knew the town sufficiently well to select a quiet parking place overlooking the harbour.

He was a fascinating companion. He boasted a fund of interesting stories and seemed to know a little about everything. Fortunately, he was not a boastful type and it was during this conversation that he reminded me of the part played by the little man who sat in the little office at the end of Strensford's ancient swing bridge.

From our vantage point, we could see the bridge. It was of Victorian vintage and spanned the middle harbour, the only link between the east and west sides of the town. Being old-fashioned it was operated by the man who sat in the tiny round hut at one end. When a ship came into the harbour and wished to proceed into the upper reaches to berth it had to make its presence known to the bridge man. He would then open the bridge to allow it through. Passages of this kind were done only at high tide, and, as high tide varied from day to day, the town was frequently brought to a standstill as a slow-moving ship sailed upstream between the open halves of the bridge. There was nothing anyone could do about it, and the bridge became a popular tourist sight.

"I'll show you something," he said when we had finished our meal. He started the engine and drove down to the harbour side where he parked in the shadows of the fish sheds with the lights off. "See the little hut on the bridge?"

"Yes," I said, for I knew it well.

"The bridge man will be in there now. It's manned for two hours either side of high tide. I can see his light on."

He flicked the switch of the PA and proceeded to give a first-rate imitation of a ship's hooter. He gave three blasts, each very slowly and each reverberating above the sleeping roofs of the town. To my ears it was a perfect reproduction of a ship's hooter and I felt sure the population of Strensford would never know it was a fake.

"That was good," I said sincerely.

"Watch the little hut," he smiled, getting out his faithful pipe.

After a few minutes a little man rushed out, peered into the darkness of the lower harbour and then uncoupled some links at the centre of the bridge. He remained on the half nearest our side of the water and I watched the massive bridge begin to open. He had set the mechanism in motion before emerging and, very slowly the two halves split at the centre, each swinging open and moving the entire structure to the sides of the river. When it was fully open the halves halted and I could see the figure of the little man standing expectantly on the edge of his half. He was peering towards the sea.

Rupert started the car engine and drove out of the fish sheds. When he was on the road, he switched on his headlights and cruised towards the bridge where a closed gate prevented sleepy drivers leaping off the edge and into the water.

"Evening, Harry," he got out and shouted at the fellow, who still gazed out to sea.

"Morning, Mr Langley. You haven't seen a ship down there, have you?"

"Not where we've been," smiled Rupert, strolling to the gate and leaning on it.

"I could swear a hooter went, honest."

"Hooter?"

"Aye, a ship's hooter, three blasts. The signal to open the bridge. Didn't you hear it?"

Rupert shook his head solemnly. "Not me, Harry."

"It must be my age," said Harry walking towards us. He remained with us for about three minutes, during which time no ship materialised from the darkness.

"I'm going barmy," he said and re-entered his little hut to set in motion the machinery to close the bridge. He repeatedly uttered sighs and said he couldn't understand it; he could have sworn he'd heard the signal to open up. Rupert never made the bridge man any wiser and we each received a cup of tea from him. We whiled away an hour in his company, listening to tales of his seafaring days. Like all old men he loved to reminisce.

And so it went on, each night producing another sound from the strangely constructed throat and lips of PC Rupert Langley. He imitated the crowing cockerel of dawn and I'm sure many a worker has rushed off early because of it. He did a useful motorcycle scrambling sound and wasn't bad with a corn horn. Howling dogs and braying donkeys were easy, and, on one occasion, he excited an entire coachload of day-trippers.

This happened in Eltering during a night patrol. The party had enjoyed a full and merry day at the seaside, having concluded their outing with a visit to a late-night club. They had left the club around two in the morning and their coach stopped at an all-night cafe in Eltering for toilets, tea and coffee. Their choice was a transport cafe, very pleasantly clean and a point of attraction for night-duty policemen.

The truth is that we fancied a cup of tea about 3.30 that morning and decided to visit that same cafe. We arrived in the carpark just as the trippers' bus began to disgorge its load. Before we had time to climb from our vehicle the entire contents of the coach had formed a long queue in the narrow doorway. It stretched halfway across the carpark, and the solitary fellow on duty would take ages to cope with this lot. We remained in the car, watching the queue with sorrow. The more we thought about our lost cups of tea the more thirsty we became.

Then I saw Rupert's eyes twinkling. Out came his pipe, which he lit among clouds of pungent fumes and, as I guessed, he picked up the handset. What was he up to now?

With the handset close to his mouth he began to produce a sound like a distant wind. It whistled slightly, then gradually intensified and changed its note. Now it was just like a jet aircraft. As Rupert increased the volume of the noise, I realised that the tail-enders of the tea queue were all peering up at the sky, seeking the elusive and noisy aircraft.

The note grew louder. Then he changed its pitch. Suddenly he produced another sound as if the engine was spluttering and backfiring. It sounded as if an aeroplane was coughing alarmingly, and he followed with a high-pitched whistling, for all the world like a crashing and doomed aircraft. The bewildered queue was buzzing with excitement and anticipation, with all eyes raised to the dark mysterious heavens as the unknown aircraft entered its final seconds.

Then the crash. How he produced this I do not know, but he crouched over the handset with his hands cupped about his mouth as he produced the most realistic and horrendous sounds of an aircraft in its final agony. He followed this masterpiece with the muffled roar of its inevitable crash, accompanied with more distant rumblings and explosions.

Then there was a long period of extreme silence. The queue members were stunned and bewildered.

"Let's go," he announced.

Lights blazing and two-tone horn blaring he spun the wheels of the police car as he emerged from the carpark, wheels and tyres shrieking as he vanished along the road. A matter of yards away he turned suddenly right. I had no idea what he was up to, but once off the main road he manoeuvred the car through the back lanes of a housing estate and minutes later reappeared at the cafe. He doused his lights and waited a short distance away.

All the waiting queue members were scrambling aboard their bus, with the driver urging them to hurry. Then the bus raced off the way we had just travelled, everyone anxiously seeking the scene of the plane crash. When it had gone, we pulled into the carpark for the second time, parked and emerged triumphant from our seats. We were enjoying a lovely cup of tea by the time the bus returned. Everyone was in a state of high excitement, and we said it was a false alarm. We couldn't explain the noises they'd heard.

It was a foregone conclusion that one night something would go wrong. A talent of that kind used in these circumstances must inevitably bring trouble of some kind, and I think Rupert knew this. His twinkling sense of humour and love of people and their reactions kept his talent within reasonable limits and it is fair to say that no harm was ever done. He knew when to stop and many victims of his jokes never knew they had been hoaxed. Many of his impressions resulted in little more than talking points or unexplained mysteries.

It was said that the inspector and the sergeants knew about his activities, but he always took care to practise his deception when no supervisory ranks were around. Very occasionally he would direct something specifically towards them. He could imitate footsteps, for example, and I've seen him sit in his car in the shadows and imitate a woman's high heels clip-clopping along a footpath. And I've seen the smile of expectancy on Sergeant Bairstow's face as he waited for the vision of loveliness to appear. Then Rupert would materialise instead. I've known him imitate a galloping horse at night with the same result. It was all good, harmless fun.

But in the early hours of one spring morning things went wrong. I was with him at the time and can smile now, although it provided a few hair-raising moments.

It was a lovely morning in late April and we had almost completed a full night's tour of duty, being scheduled to come off patrol at six o'clock. It was about a quarter to five and the sun was striving to make the coming day warm and beautiful. The dew of night covered the choice grass about us and the birds were waking the countryside, all competing for the crown of champion of the morning chorus.

We had concluded a long, careful patrol of the district and had a few minutes to spare before returning to Ashfordly, where I would book off duty. Rupert brought the car to rest on a small hillock at the side of a rural lane, a vantage point regularly used by sightseers during fine weekends. It provided a fine view of Ryedale and was perfect for a picnic. Behind us were the open moorlands, stretching loftily into North Yorkshire, but before us, on the bottom side of the road, was a pasture full of very contended cows. As we parked, they peered balefully at us, as cows tend to do, and one or two took a step nearer out of sheer curiosity. This is a feature of cows — they do like to know what's going on, but within a few minutes they had accepted as harmless the big black shiny creature with bright eyes. They returned their attention to the succulent grass.

There must have been fifty all told. They were all chewing their cud and munching very noisily without a care in the world. Their only worry would be milking-time in a couple of hours or so, followed by a gentle meander back to this field. It was a life of sheer pleasantry, and these cows looked very satisfied with their lives.

"I can do a lovely randy bull noise," announced Rupert, taking out his pipe.

I laughed. "Randy bull noise?"

"A bellow, I think it's termed. It has quite a dramatic effect on cows, you know, particularly in the spring."

"Has it?" I wasn't convinced.

"That's when a young cow's fancy lightly turns to thoughts of randy bulls," he said.

I chuckled at his description. "What happens?"

"I'll show you."

With no more ado he laid his pipe to one side, switched on the PA and cupped the handset in his hands. He bent to his task and there emerged from the loudspeaker on our front bumper the most awful bellowing noise. I watched the cows. Without exception they pricked their ears and looked in our direction. As one they stared at the big black bull who was calling to them so lovingly.

"See! I've got their attention!" he smiled, returning to his task.

He repeated the love-sick bellowing and the amplified noise echoed about the landscape. The cows loved it. They began to walk towards us. The entire herd was moving.

He repeated the exercise, his eyes closed tightly with concentration as he fought to produce exactly the right sound. By now, the herd was in full gallop, responding to his music . . .

"Hey!" I nudged him. "They're coming for us . . ."

"Just curiosity," he replied. "Cows are like that," and he didn't look up from his work as he began another love-call. This final one galvanised the eager cows into a frenzy of activity, and the entire herd was now in full flight and heading for our car.

At the approaching thunder of hooves he looked up.

"God!" he cried, and in an instant started the engine. He rammed it into first gear and we roared from our vantage point as the leading cow crashed through the fragile hawthorn hedge in a passion of lust. She was followed by all the others and as we roared along the road the entire herd galloped after us.

My final memory that night is our speeding car tearing along a rural lane, hotly pursued by fifty love-sick maidens, all with their tails in the air.

Thus ended my first lesson with the Road Traffic Division.

CHAPTER SEVEN

Keep the home fires burning while
your hearts are yearning.
LENA GUILBERT FORD — "Keep the
Home Fires Burning"

In their early days some police forces combined law enforcement with firefighting and indeed many pioneer police officers were equally skilled in both roles. As the police became more professional and their area of responsibility more specific their firefighting duties were cast aside. Today the Fire Brigades and the Police Service work side by side at many incidents and indeed continue to share buildings in some places. The modern policeman does not possess a fund of stories connected with firefighting, although I do like this old yarn.

In the days when police did fight fires a large blaze broke out in a well-known store in York, and the police were called to the scene. Unfortunately, their horses were all engaged upon a ceremonial occasion and none was available to haul the firefighting appliance to the fire. Undeterred, the chief rushed into the street and halted the first vehicle he saw, a large cart drawn by two equally large horses. He commandeered these for the job.

After skilfully harnessing them to the fire-tender the fire-fighters climbed aboard and whipped the surprised horses into a gallop. Unaccustomed as they were in this task the gallant animals responded magnificently and were soon galloping through the quaint streets, en route to the blazing building.

The machine careered across the River Ouse bridge, and there was the fire. The driver tried to bring his team to a halt, but they were having none of that! They continued past the seat of the fire and, in spite of yells, shouts, whips and other methods, they refused to stop. The horses eventually ran themselves to a standstill some three miles on the road to Tadcaster. From that date spare horses were available in case of emergencies.

When I joined the Force those days had long passed, and the Fire Brigade was a modernised unit noted for its extraordinary speed, coupled with sheer efficiency and ability. Even though we were two quite distinct organisations, however, the police initial training course contained instructions on how the police should cooperate with the Fire Brigade.

If my memory has not faded, a complete lesson was devoted to the police duties and responsibilities at fires. This was considered necessary because the work of a police officer inevitably brings him to the scene of most fires and it was, and still is, essential that a patrolling bobby knows what to do when faced with an emergency of this kind.

We were taught that, when patrolling our beats, we had to familiarise ourselves with the locations of all turncocks, principal fire hydrants and their water supplies. For the latter we often relied on rivers, canals, reservoirs, tanks and the like. We had to know the local procedures for calling out the Fire Brigade and were exhorted to discover the whereabouts of essential equipment like blankets, ropes, sheets, sand, tarpaulins, sacks, ladders, buckets and a host of other useful things.

Another aspect of our local knowledge was that we were expected to know who was likely to be in a particular building at any one time, or who to contact out of normal office hours.

It was always useful to know if a building had a resident caretaker and which buildings were deserted at night, weekends, holidays or other times. The intricacies of emergency firefighting apparatus had to be understood and it was prudent to visit buildings with a view to learning the location and *modus operandi* of those items.

All this was drummed into us at Training School in a one-hour lesson and we were then compelled to learn, parrot-fashion, our responsibilities at the scene of a fire. These were resolutely hammered into our brains, just as children learn their arithmetic tables and alphabet. The result was that we never forgot them. I remember our responsibilities, for they conveniently provided ten answers, which made them a very handy examination question.

They were:

(a) ascertain whether the fire service has been called; if so, by whom. If not, do so IMMEDIATELY;

(b) save human life;

(c) save animal life;

(d) save and protect property;

(e) prevent stealing;

(f) assist the Fire Brigade;

(g) divert traffic where necessary;

(h) keep a record of important matters;

(i) if the building is unattended, inform the owners or key-holders;

(j) in large outbreaks, ensure police reinforcements are available.

Once those points were firmly implanted in our brains it was deemed acceptable to turn us loose to hunt for fires. In reality, there was a lot more to the practical application of our duties, but those ten points did remain implanted in the brains of police officers who assisted at fires. It was rather like checking off a shopping-list.

In addition to those pertinent points there was the responsibility of knowing what to do at the scene if we were the first to arrive. For example, we had to attempt to cut off the fire's supply of air, we had to search buildings for casualties and beware of weakened walls or floors. In the event of chimney fires we were advised to help the householder remove the fire from the grate and shift any inflammable material from the vicinity of the fireplace. Rugs, furniture, curtains and so forth had to be taken away from the heat and one suggested method of stifling the blaze was to shove wet sacks up the chimney. I learned that finding wet sacks was never easy.

We must always be aware of the risk of inhaling smoke or lethal fumes and were told to crawl about burning buildings on our hands and knees to avoid those problems. This is the advice given:

"Remember, heat rises and with it, smoke. When in smoke, CRAWL and keep your nose and mouth near the floor. You will get air, you will see, and you will not trip up."

I felt it was sound advice and it did provide a memorable mental picture of a firefighting constable. We were taught that the best way to remove an unconscious person from a smoke-filled room is to drag him along the floor. This could be done by tying the casualty's hands about one's neck and crawling with him between one's legs. The advice continued, "Proceed downstairs backwards, supporting the patient's head and shoulders." It was all good stirring stuff.

To escape from upstairs windows we had to lower ourselves until hanging by the fingertips on the window ledge then kick backwards and drop with bended knees. We had to beware of arson and therefore preserve what we could at the scene, like cans of paraffin, matches, electrical devices and so forth. We were reminded of the various legal rules appertaining to fires. For example, at that time it was an automatic offence for anyone in a town to allow a chimney to catch fire, and it was equally illegal for anyone to knowingly make a false alarm call.

Like firemen, the police had certain powers to enter premises in which a fire had broken out or was suspected when entry was necessary for the purpose of extinguishing fire, and this could be done without the consent of unhelpful, obstructive or absent owners or occupiers. If necessary, we could break in. Furthermore, the senior police officer present could close any street or regulate traffic whenever necessary or desirable for firefighting purposes, and, in the absence of a police officer, those powers were given to the senior fire officer.

Armed with this kind of close knowledge about my powers, duties and responsibilities I sallied forth into the world beyond Training School and felt rather more confident than some of my colleagues, so far as firefighting was concerned. This was because as a member of the Royal Air Force during my National Service, I had compulsorily attended a two-week firefighting course near Blackpool. There we were lectured about the various types of fires, about methods of putting them out, about how to shout, "Water On" and "Water Off" at the right time, how to hold a hose as the power of water was pumped through, and how to climb ladders correctly.

In a rural area like Aidensfield, however, all this knowledge and training could be wasted. The likelihood of a fire was remote, or so I thought.

As it happened, they seemed to break out all over the place. I doubt if there were more than usual in other places, but a village policeman knows everything that happens, and whereas most fires do not reach the ken of the public because they are minor ones, they are made known to the local police officer, even if they are nothing more than chip-pans bursting into conflagrations.

One of my first problems with a fire occurred at the Moorcock Inn, some miles beyond my village. It lies on a lonely road which spans the spacious heights of the North Yorkshire moors. It is a fine old coaching inn of considerable interest, and one of its noted and much publicised claims to fame was its peat-fire.

Peat provides a most useful fuel in moorland homes. It burns very slowly and steadily and throws out a considerable heat. It is dug from the moors after which the square turves are neatly piled into stacks to allow the wind to pass through and dry them. These are known locally as "rickles" or even "rooks" and can be seen dotted across the windswept heights.

When the peat is dry it makes a beautiful fire. It is enhanced by an interesting smell which is a permanent feature of peat-burning homes and which can sometimes be recognised at a distance when tramping across the moors. Many a sensitive nose had identified peat-smoke rising from isolated chimney stacks.

The Moorcock Inn, being very isolated and therefore liable to be cut off for weeks in the winter, solved its heating problems by burning peat. Outside the cosy inn numerous heaps of peat were stacked while inside the bar was a traditional peat-fire complete with traditional peat-smell. That fire has burned through some of the worst winters on record and even though local coal supplies have failed to reach the inn the establishment remained warm and cosy, a true bastion of delight against the storms outside. Just as it had sheltered marooned coaching-parties in bygone days, so it now offered the same hospitality to lone motorists or even modern coach-parties.

It was a modern coach-party which created something of a storm *within* that peaceful place. At the time, the inn was not cut off by snow, although it was a bleak winter's night when the party arrived. The coach was full of young men, about forty in number, and within seconds that peaceful rural haven was transformed into a maelstrom of arms, legs, tongues and shaking heads, accompanied by loud voices and hearty laughter. Clearly, members of the party were enjoying themselves and very soon the strong Yorkshire beer did much to further that happy state.

In their mellow mood it was not long before the cheerful bunch discovered the history of the peat-fire burning so gracefully and pungently in the grate beside them. Legend said that the fire had never stopped burning for 125 years; it had burned continually during that time in spite of hot and cold days, fuel shortages, sick landlords, tired and lazy staff and spells of isolation during the long winters.

As interest mounted in this piece of history it transpired that the boisterous party was a rugby football team and its supporters. A reputation of the kind enjoyed by this fire presented a challenge to these men — if that fire had burned for a century and a quarter it seemed to be their earthbound duty to extinguish it. A rapid conference was held and, within minutes, six volunteers stepped forward to put out that ancient moorland blaze. The method proposed was to do so in the manner expected of a beer-swilling rugby football team.

The six stood proudly before the smouldering chunks of peat and in spite of angry representations from the unhappy landlord they opened their trousers, took out their hoses and promptly began the task of extinguishing the fire. Their team mates gave them valuable support during this performance and shouted encouragement from the ranks while a second team stood by to continue should the first effort end in failure.

I arrived not by choice but by coincidence. By then the deed had been done and the merry coach had left for a famous West Riding of Yorkshire town, noted for its own strong beer and rugby team. Unaware of these very recent events I walked into a bar seething with furious locals and reeking of something which was definitely not peat-fumes. When I expressed my distaste at the aroma the landlord told his sorry tale and led me to the fireplace. Its contents looked dead. The old stone hearth contained little pools of liquid and the lumps of half-burned peat showed no signs of life. I knew I was witnessing the end of an historic era.

One hundred and twenty-five years of history had been snuffed out within seconds. It was not surprising that the regulars were very, very angry and complained bitterly to me. I turned to the landlord and asked,

"Is this an official complaint?"

"Is it summat you can deal with?" he asked.

"Not really," I said, racking my brains to determine whether it was a criminal offence to urinate upon a peat-fire. I wondered if the actions qualified as malicious damage to a fire but knew of no such provision although there was a possibility that their actions could be construed as "conduct likely to cause a breach of the peace". This is an offence which can occur only in a public place, so that raised the question of whether a bar was a public place . . .

"There must be summat I can do about it," he said, ruffling his hair. "They've ruined my main feature — folks come miles to see that fire. It's the longest burning fire in the country, and they've put it out! That's criminal! It must be. There must be summat you can do!"

"I think it's a civil matter," I pronounced. "You should see your solicitor — he might be able to claim damages or compensation for you."

"That's no good," he snorted. "It'll take ages to fix that, and besides, there's no guarantee I'd win, is there?"

"In that case, it hasn't been put out, has it?" I stated firmly.

"It has, there's not a sign of life. See for yourself."

"It's still burning," I said to him, equally firmly and hoping he would get my message. "They didn't succeed, did they? In spite of their watery efforts, your peat-fire is still burning."

One of the regulars, an old farmer with skin like leather and a curved walking-stick in his hand, said, "Nay, it's nut oot, Harry. It's bonning yit. Ah can see it. It just needs a spot o' help

"You could tell the local papers," I suggested. "Imagine the publicity — a team of West Riding rugger players trying to put out a North Riding peat-fire that's burned for a century and a quarter — and failing. You've got all these witnesses who'll swear to that failure, hasn't he, lads? You wouldn't let Lancastrians put it out, would you?"

The others, including the landlord, remained silent, not apparently understanding the import of my statement. I tried again.

"The fire didn't go out, did it?" I spelled out the situation. "Those silly bloody rugger players did not succeed, did they? We couldn't let 'em beat this pub, could we? You're all witnesses — you can all say they failed, can't you?"

And then they all laughed.

"By lad, thoo's reet," said one of them, and the gnarled old fellow with the stick stooped to peer into the smelly grate. "It's bonning yit!" he said smugly. "Nay, Harry, them daft buggers didn't kill it."

As Harry went back to his bar feeling happier, if a little puzzled, we collected a few pieces of paper, some dry kindling sticks from the shed behind the pub, and we gave a burst of assistance to the struggling peat. The underparts had not been dampened, and very soon, the peat ignited and returned to its old smouldering ways.

I did wonder whether the challenge would be accepted by lots more passing teams and suggested that Harry placed a second fire in an outbuilding especially for them to pee on. He said he'd consider it.

A local paper got hold of the tale and published a lovely piece about the resilience of the fire and it gained some valuable publicity for the inn. Even today the pub boasts of its longest-living peat-fire, about which legend says that not even a noted rugby team and several gallons of strong Yorkshire beer could extinguish.

The next fire I had to cope with occurred in the early hours of one morning while I was on duty at Eltering. It had been a very peaceful night with no occurrences and by three o'clock I was beginning to feel rather bored and tired.

Then I smelled smoke.

As I stood beside the telephone kiosk outside Eltering Post Office I could smell smoke. It was drifting from somewhere behind the main street, apparently from a clutch of buildings although the darkness made it impossible to see its source. I wandered up and down the street, sniffing the night air while trying to trace its origin.

Then I heard a voice behind me.

"What's going on, Rhea? You're like a bloody greyhound, sniffing like that."

Sergeant Blaketon had emerged from one of the alleys in time to see my perambulations with nose aloft.

"I can smell smoke, Sergeant. It's not far away."

"It'll be a bonfire," he said. "Somebody will have lit a bonfire and it'll be smouldering. They do that, you know."

"It's not that sort of smell," I insisted. It wasn't a bonfire smell. Bonfires have their own distinctive smell, and this was different. It is difficult to describe a smell, but I knew this was definitely not a bonfire. I continued to parade up and down the street, sniffing and looking for signs of smoke. He joined me, and together we promenaded, noses in the air, sniffing loudly. It must have been a strange sight.

"Bonfire," he said eventually. "I can smell it now. Bonfire, Rhea."

"No, Sergeant," I argued. "It is not a bonfire!" and then I saw the faintest wisp of grey smoke drifting past the illuminated windows of the telephone kiosk. "There!" I pointed. "It's floating past the kiosk."

"Bonfire," he affirmed.

I decided to explore. I was very unhappy about this for it was most certainly a strange smell, not the scent of burning garden rubbish. By peering into the night sky against the reflection of the town's few remaining lights I hoped to catch sight of more drifting smoke. And I did. I saw a considerable plume rising from an area tucked in the middle of a cluster of ancient buildings, just behind the main street.

"There!" I pointed out the grey pall to Sergeant Blaketon.

I galloped towards it. That part of Eltering is a maze of narrow passages and tiny alleys where dozens of small houses are literally clustered on top of one another. Their age and construction means they are tinder dry, their old wooden roofs and beamed ceilings being perfect fuel for a major blaze. And I knew there were no gardens in that part of town. This was no bonfire.

Blaketon followed my urgent dash and I could hear him panting through the dark passages. We didn't know where we were going for each passage had others leading from it, and in those narrow confines I could not see the smoke against the night sky. I was guided by my sense of smell and the smell was intensifying. Now I heard the crackling of flames.

Round the very next bend I found it. It was a narrow cottage tucked into the corner of an alley and it was half-timbered. Through its ancient mullioned window I could see the glow of a fierce blaze. The entire room was burning brightly and the upper storey window was missing, casting a thickening blanket of smoke across the nearby roofs. Sergeant Blaketon arrived seconds later and we stood for a moment, awestruck at the sight of this tiny cottage as its interior glowed a fierce and menacing red.

"Fire Brigade!" he gasped. "Police — ring for them too, Malton."

I galloped back to the kiosk and dialled three nines for the Fire Brigade before panting out my story. I was out of breath and had difficulty gasping out the address but soon convinced the recipient of the urgency of my call. I told the police at Malton and asked for assistance; rapid help was assured.

I ran back to the scene and found Sergeant Blaketon, his face glistening with perspiration in the red glow, knocking on doors and attempting to rouse the sleeping occupants of adjoining premises. He was running up and down, thumping doors and shouting, "Fire, fire . . ."

I did likewise.

In the light provided by the blaze I could see more of the burning cottage. It was tucked into a corner of a small, cobbled square deep in the heart of old Eltering. All around were lots of similar buildings, all with tiny windows, old doors and low ceilings, ancient and tinder dry. If this fire spread . . . It reminded me of the Great Fire of London . . . the potential inferno didn't bear thinking about.

"It's a warehouse," Sergeant Blaketon yelled above the roar of flames. "Full of toys and games. Nobody inside, thank God . . ."

Although we knocked on neighbouring doors nobody responded. Not one person answered. The Fire Brigade arrived very quickly and soon had their thick hoses snaking through the passages. Men in dark uniforms and shining helmets arrived and the place became a hive of organised activity. Firemen with breathing apparatus and powerful lights battered their way into the blazing building to search for casualties as I continued to knock on doors.

As we worked a senior fire officer halted us. "You'll have to evacuate these houses," he ordered. "If this blaze gets away from us the whole lot'll go up. People an' all. I hope we can contain it but . . ." and his voice tailed away.

We tried again. I counted the cottages in question. There were only six. I had been to every one several times and so had Oscar Blaketon. We were beginning to think they were all empty, perhaps kept as holiday cottages and then I heard the swish of curtains being drawn open. I looked up and a man's face appeared at a bedroom window. He glowed orange in the bright light.

"Out!" I shouted above the noise and saw the horror on his face as he stared at the blazing inferno only yards away. "Out — anybody else in there?"

The face vanished, and I hammered on more doors. By now there was a tremendous amount of noise at the scene — firemen were working and shouting, water was hissing, fire crackling, timbers falling, slates crashing and Sergeant Blaketon hammering on doors with his truncheon. How anyone could sleep through this din I do not know. If it took our combined efforts to rouse the orange-faced individual, there could be more people in bed, so I concentrated on the house which had produced the face.

As I hammered, a frightened feminine face appeared, wearing long blonde hair. "Out!" I cried at the top of my voice, cupping my mouth with my hands. "Hurry up, for God's sake . . ."

She vanished, but still no one emerged.

Anxious firemen were rattling doors, banging dustbins and generally creating as much noise as possible. At last it had some effect. More curtains opened, more glowing faces appeared, and more people began to move about inside those threatened houses.

"Take 'em away, out into the main street, for safety," Sergeant Blaketon ordered. "Get their names, ask how many folks were inside. Everyone must be accounted for."

The senior fire officer was dutifully organising his men and other nearby residents who had arrived to watch as I moved away from the immediate vicinity. I stood aside, and my little group of bewildered people began to grow as the startled sleepers emerged from their six tiny houses. All wore casual clothes — sweaters and light trousers — and as they assembled in a huddle near me, I asked, "Anyone left inside?"

No one spoke. They were all too shocked.

I called to Sergeant Blaketon. "Sergeant," I cried. "Can we check inside every cottage, one by one? I think they're all here now."

A fireman answered. "Aye," he said and promptly vanished inside the nearest. As he did this a couple emerged from another and soon, I had six shivering couples standing around me. We waited as the fireman bobbed in and out of the houses and eventually declared every one empty.

Meanwhile three fire appliances had parked in the street and their long, snaking hoses were pumping gallons of water into the blazing building. The firemen were doing a good job, their chief mission being to prevent the spread of flames. I felt they were gaining the upper hand.

"Come on," I said to my group. "I've got to check you all."

Like sheep the six men and six girls followed me along the dark alley until we arrived in the main street, aglow with lights and throbbing with action as the three appliances worked their way into the coming dawn. From the safety of the street I could see the dull red glow that now brightened the sky, and the flicker of red at the distant end of the passage.

People were standing around in nightclothes, and in the midst of all the activity and interest I drew my little notebook from my pocket, moved the survivors into a shop doorway and prepared to count them.

"Well," I tried to be cheerful. "You're all safe. I'll need your names, please, for accounting purposes. We'll have to make a detailed inspection of every affected house and premises to check for missing persons. It's routine."

No one spoke.

I wondered if they were all in a state of deep shock.

"Come along," I coaxed them. "Names. How about you?"

I addressed a young man with a mop of untidy hair. He looked at the others and his facial expression told me that something was not quite as it should be. I then looked at his companions. Six pretty girls. Six young men. Six young men with six pretty girls, all shy.

Who owned the cottages? I did not know because Eltering was not part of my own regular beat and these night visits provided only a cursory knowledge of the town.

I slowly looked them up and down.

"Local folks?" I asked.

The one I had addressed shook his head. "No," he said. "We're on holiday."

"A conference, actually," chipped in a second youngster, a man.

And a girl giggled.

"Look," I said, my notebook open in the palm of my hand, "I've got to take your names because I've got to check the safety of everyone. That's all."

I was recalling the ten points I'd learned at Training School, one of which was to keep a record of important matters. I reckoned this was important.

The first man gave me his name. I noted it and asked for his address. "This address, you mean?"

"Isn't this your home address?" I put to him.

"Do we have to? Give our home addresses?" he asked.

I was beginning to understand.

"Look," I said firmly. "All I'm concerned about is the safety of the people in those cottages. Why you are here does not concern me. If something is bothering you," and I looked from one to the other, "then say so. I'm discreet enough not to let anything slip, if that's bothering you. If I know your problem I can cope with it. If I don't know it . . ." I left the phrase unfinished.

"Okay," the spokesman said. "I'm staying at No 3."

"What's the alley's name? I asked.

"Cross Alley," he said. "Houses two to seven are rented as holiday accommodation. No 1 is that store, a toy-shop store. They're all owned by the same man, the shopkeeper. We've rented the cottages for a holiday. There's no more of us — just the twelve."

"So there's no problem. Now, names, please."

Full appreciation of their dilemma now dawned on me. Not one of these men was married to the girl with whom he had been discovered. One could now understand their reluctance to leave the cottages in spite of the threat by fire, and I've no doubt they all hoped it would be extinguished before it led to the discovery of their love-nests. But things don't work out quite like that.

I took down their names, with two of the girls crying softly into their boyfriends' arms, and eventually Sergeant Blaketon appeared and asked, "All safe?"

"All accounted for, Sergeant," I said with confidence.

"Smashing. They've got the fire under control. The cottage will be a wreck, a total loss I'd say, and the contents.

Looks like an electrical fault. You folks will be all back soon. They've stopped it spreading. Panic's over."

An hour later I was sitting in No 3 with the young man to whom I had first spoken and his girlfriend. Three firemen were with me, all enjoying cups of tea and biscuits. Sergeant Blaketon and another police sergeant from Malton were in another cottage, and in every house a little party was being held. Outside a pair of vigilant firemen continued to play their hoses into the gutted cottage and kept the smouldering heap of burnt-out toys from breaking into a new blaze.

By six o'clock that morning it was all over. The firemen had gone, and I was alone with my young couple.

"Thanks for the tea," I prepared to leave too. "Sorry you've been disturbed."

"It won't get into the papers, will it?" asked the girl, called Susan.

"The fire? I reckon it will. It'll be in all the local papers."

"Oh God!" she cried. "I hope my husband doesn't find out."

"He won't, Sue," the man curled his arm about her. "I'm in the same boat — my Anne thinks I'm at a conference."

"Your names won't be released." I was the only person with their names. "If the Press do ring tomorrow your names won't be released by us. If they call here don't tell them who you are and don't allow them to take your pictures. Just say you are all safe and intend to continue your holidays."

"I'll tell the others. Thanks."

"Don't mention it, but," I smiled, "off the record, who are you?"

"Office workers," he said, smiling ruefully. "Income tax officials, actually. The chap with this block of cottages owns a shop, as I said. We know him. He let us all book in — we're six mates from one office — and we said to our wives that we were going off to a conference. These are six girls from the office — they said the same to their folks. Delicate, you see."

"Very delicate," I agreed.

I felt like asking if any of them worked on my income tax returns, but my question might have been misinterpreted. I remained silent and wished them a happy conference, or perhaps I should have said congress.

But I still wonder if any of those youngsters deal with my income tax returns.

A strange provision relating to fires was drummed into us at Training School, where we were told that it was illegal to allow one's chimney to catch fire. Anyone whose chimney did catch fire was therefore to be reported and summoned to appear before the local magistrates' court. If they were found guilty the fine would be a maximum of ten shillings (50p). The statute which created this offence was the Town Police Clauses Act of 1847 which was, and still is, in force in some urban areas. One major problem was learning which urban areas were affected; furthermore, it did not apply to rural districts. This meant that rural chimneys could happily catch fire and belch forth smoke without offending against this law, although the Public Health Act of 1936 did create something called a "smoke nuisance". This could be dealt with by a local authority.

Smoke nuisances of the latter kind were not of great concern to the patrolling policeman, although reported chimney fires did mean a visit to the house in question for the purpose of reporting the unfortunate individual whose chimney had let him down. More often than not the case never reached court as the offender would receive an official written caution from the Chief Constable. This was infinitely better than facing a court.

It must be said that few policemen sought chimney fires; official notification was left to the Fire Brigade, some of whose officers seemed to enjoy reporting these minor disasters to us so that the necessary legal procedures could be implemented.

In the rural areas, however, it did not really matter to the policeman whether or not a chimney caught fire. It was not illegal on my beat and my time at Aidensfield did not involve me in any such crisis. Certainly, there were chimney fires and much surplus smoke was cast high into the heavens, but summonses were never issued.

Another factor was that country folk were rather particular about keeping their chimneys clean. They employed some ingenious methods to maintain them in a clean condition, and a good old rural recipe was to burn potato peelings in the fireplace with a dash of salt. This was to prevent an accumulation of soot in the chimney. Many rural men swept their own chimneys, having purchased the necessary equipment, and there were others who reckoned such expenditure was unnecessary.

Instead, they adopted natural methods, one of which was to obtain a thick bunch of holly and lash it tightly together so that a kind of rough broom head was formed. Ideally it should be wider than the chimney. It was then tied to a long rope, and in order to use this device, two people were needed. One carried the holly to the top of the chimney and perched this on the rim. The rope thus dangled down inside, and the second man seized the end. He then pulled it down inside the chimney and his mate pulled it up again. This was a very effective brushing device but there is nothing to indicate how the man at the bottom kept himself clean. It was reckoned to be a good system for those rural folk who burned only wood because wood-burning residue rested in all kinds of places within the chimney breast. The springiness of the holly was sure to remove it.

Another system was to obtain a large piece of holly and ensure it was dry. It was then lit so that it burned fiercely and cast via the fireplace up into the chimney. If things worked out correctly the rising draught would carry the blazing object right up the chimney and out at the top thus dislodging the soot along its roaring route. If the holly lodged along its route, the chimney might catch fire, but this served the same purpose, if a little dramatically.

One of the finest methods was to carry a live hen to the top of the chimney and drop it down. Its urgent flapping during the descent removed all the surplus soot which promptly fell into the hearth and often spilled into the room. If one was not careful, the hen, very relieved at reaching base, ran about in sheer happiness and left a trail of soot as it squawked and flapped in blessed joy. I have no recipe for cleaning sooty hens.

If rural folks had recipes for cleaning chimneys, they also had recipes for putting out chimney fires. The simplest was to shut all doors and windows and stop up the bottom of the chimney with a piece of sacking saturated in water. In addition some would throw salt on to the fire with sulphur if available. This was considered a good substance to throw into the grate if the chimney was blazing because it exhausted the fire's supply of oxygen. This seemed a favourite method because the fire starved itself to death.

I have seen chimney fires roaring like jet aircraft, and at times the chimney stack has grown practically red hot with smoke and flames belching out. Such fires are fed from below by powerful draughts which produce the roaring noise. Surprisingly, little or no damage is done, but one problem in the countryside is that many cottages were built in such a way that timber sometimes entered the chimney breast. The ends of the beams were exposed in the chimney and many farms have wooden beams beneath their fireplaces. Lots of old chimneys have ledges and shelves inside, the outcome of rough building techniques, and if burning soot accumulates in those areas the result can be danger to the house. Hens or burning holly were useless if these areas got alight; the only answer was lots of water.

A chimney fire of this kind occurred in a small terraced house at Aidensfield as I was patrolling the village. I was first upon the scene. The cottage belonged to a retired postman called Horace Hart, a widower who kept his home immaculate. It seemed he'd forgotten to arrange the annual sweeping of his chimney, and when I arrived it was well alight, belching forth magnificent clouds of dense black smoke in spite of the wet sack Horace had stuffed aloft.

He had called the Fire Brigade from a neighbour's house and I decided to await its arrival. There was nothing anyone could do in the meantime. Ashfordly Fire Brigade comprised a happy band of part-timers who had to leave their daytime jobs or their firesides and rush to the Fire Station, praying earnestly that their fire appliance would start.

As this was late one evening with men about their homes I felt reasonably confident that the brigade would make it. As a crowd gathered to observe events, Horace's chimney was puffing out huge clouds in fine style. It was a classic chimney fire.

Among the neighbours who gathered to watch was the man in the adjoining cottage. His interest was not difficult to understand for he emerged spluttering and coughing his anger that such a thing could happen, especially as the two houses were linked. This was Lieutenant-Colonel (retired) Jasper Q Clarke, who lived there with his sister and who pompously strutted about the village organising the lives of others and complaining incessantly about the noise from children, aircraft, tractors, radio sets, ice-cream vans, cars, motorcycles and seagulls. Some bicycle bells also annoyed him.

Fortunately for him no one had complained about the noises made by Lieutenant-Colonel (retired) Clarke, but his anti-social activities did excite comment among the locals. He was a smart little man with a bristling grey moustache and grey hair cut in a military style. He wore hacking jackets and cavalry twill trousers, brogue shoes and occasionally a monocle. So perfectly did he play his part that sometimes I wondered if he was a confidence trickster pretending to be a retired army officer, but his credentials seemed genuine.

His presence among the observers led to comments about black deposits falling upon his garden and house and the dangers thus presented to his property by the inferno in the chimney right next to his. He kept darting into his own house to check it wasn't ablaze, and it seemed his sister was away for the evening. He had reason to worry, however, because these cottage fireplaces were back-to-back, with their chimneys rising parallel with one another. They emerged in one chimney stack, albeit with separate chimney-pots.

With the anxious little man pacing up and down, the village awaited the arrival of Ashfordly Fire Brigade. When it arrived twenty minutes later the chimney was still belching black clouds and Horace continued to dampen the sack which filled the base of his stack. Clearly, the internal timbers or sooty deposits on the ledges inside were still burning, and this was dangerous.

Unfortunately for Horace it seemed that Thirsk Races had been held that evening, and every member of the Fire Brigade save one had taken the opportunity to watch a local horse. It had won, and they had gone out celebrating; they had not yet returned. The Fire Brigade therefore arrived in the person of one man, and he was driving the appliance.

He knew it was a chimney fire before embarking upon this trip and was prepared to tackle the blaze alone, an idea that held some hope. In my capacity as local constable, however, I offered my help, casually mentioning my RAF Fire Fighting Course and the instruction received at Police Training School.

The fireman, a butcher from Ashfordly, said he appreciated my offer of assistance. He would have to operate the machinery of the fire appliance and asked if I could manage the hose. Proudly, I said I knew how to hold a nozzle and knew all about shouting "Water On" and "Water Off".

Thus the firefighting team was prepared. After inspecting the seat of the fire the fireman announced that something inside the chimney was ablaze. This confirmed our diagnosis. It might be sooty accumulations, or it might be some exposed timbers, either of which needed water to extinguish it. Horace was therefore advised to remove all his furniture from the room in question because the resultant mess would be pretty ghastly. Aided by the onlookers we had the room clear within five or ten minutes and removed the sack from the chimney. This created some extra smoke and served only to feed the fire.

Because I was operating the hose I had to climb the ladder of the fire appliance with the hose and direct the jet down the chimney. Through a series of switches on the fire appliance a ladder crept skywards until it came to rest very close to the belching chimney. My duty was simple — I had to climb the ladder in the manner taught me at the RAF Fire Fighting Course and direct the nozzle down Horace's chimney until the fire was extinguished. It was a simple task.

I began my journey. The ladder shook and trembled as I climbed in the approved style, clutching the hose in the recommended manner. Finally I reached the chimney stack. Thick smoke was pouring out and my eyes began to smart. There was barely room to breathe among the swirling clouds as they moved about me, sometimes totally enveloping me and sometimes letting me bathe in the glow of the many lights below. In spite of the heat from the chimney and in spite of the effects of the smoke and in spite of the darkness and danger, I managed to seize the nozzle in the correct hold and direct it into the chimney-pot. My eyes were aflame by this time, smarting and running with tears, I was coughing violently, my hands were burning, and I turned my head to avoid the thick, rising mass of muck and soot.

But the all-important nozzle was in position. I was ready. Half closing my eyes against the swirling, stinking cloud I reached out and by touch confirmed that the nozzle was firmly inside the chimney-pot. I shouted, "Water On".

There would be a short wait as the water rose to the occasion, and through smarting eyes, I looked down upon the little crowd below. Lieutenant-Colonel (retired) Clarke had rushed indoors yet again to check his house and all eyes were upon me. Lights and torches beamed their rays in my direction, and from my vantage point I could see the powerful jet of water thrusting its way along the hose. I watched mesmerised as the flat empty hose thickened rapidly and grew round as the water approached the nozzle. It straightened out the bends and jerked the hose into life, forcing it to kick against the strain. At that precise moment the wind changed direction and I was totally smothered in a moving mass of smoke. The hose was bucking in my grasp.

When this happens the force is tremendous and threatens to jolt the nozzle from your grasp. It must be held firm at all costs otherwise it can leap from your grasp and cause severe injuries to anyone nearby. Blinded by the smoke and heat I hung on for all I was worth. The nozzle moved within the chimney-pot — I felt it slide under the pressure, but the smoke concealed it. I clung to it as it writhed and bucked in my tight grip and listened as the powerful jet gushed down the chimney. Once it was pouring out of the nozzle I settled down to hold it tightly in position, my eyes smarting and my lips dry with the dirt and heat.

Then there was a tremendous commotion below.

Lieutenant-Colonel (retired) Jasper Q Clarke ran out of his house, smothered from head to toe in a thick black horrible mess. His eyes were the only white spots about him as they peered beseechingly from the mask fate had donated him.

I had put the hose down the wrong chimney.

CHAPTER EIGHT

And many a burglar I've restored to his
friends and his relations.
SIR WILLIAM SCHWENCK
GILBERT — *Trial by Jury*

Sir William Schwenck Gilbert (1836—1911) achieved operatic success when he worked with Sir Arthur Seymour Sullivan (1842—1900), but it was the former who coined the oft-repeated phrase about what happens when "the enterprising burglar's not aburgling". Not many other writers feature the burglar in their works — they favour murderers and confidence tricksters, highwaymen or kidnappers and in fact the burglar is frequently portrayed as a simple fellow clad in a striped sweater bearing the word "swag" across the front. In spite of the burglar's lack of appeal as a creature of drama, his deeds are dark and sinister because he breaks into the castle of man and the plain fact is that burglars are not universally loved by their public.

None the less, the burglar was greatly loved by lawyers. He made money for them because the nature of the crime lent itself to many hours of legal wrangling, discussion, fee-earning and decision-making in High Courts. He also provided legal authors with a good deal of fascinating copy while the constable in his infancy must learn and understand the intricacies of this crime.

For hundreds of years burglary could be perpetrated only at night, and this fact alone gave it a certain stature. Today things have changed, and burglary may be committed at any time of the day or night.

When I joined the police service, therefore, burglary was a night-time crime and had to be prevented at all costs. If a burglary was committed on one's beat it was considered akin to allowing a murder to happen or a rape to occur, consequently every police officer did everything in his power to prevent burglaries.

There is a certain fascination in the history of the crime. Ancient legal writers tell how houses, churches and even the walls of cities and their gates were legally protected from being breached by villains who wished to steal. Chester and York are examples of such cities. The earliest known name for the crime was *burgh-breche* and its Latin name around AD 1200 was *burgaria*. Today we would not regard breaking into cities through their walls as burglary, but it was once part of this old crime. By the Middle Ages, however, it had come to be applied only to dwelling-houses, although for a time churches were encompassed within its provisions because they were regarded as the dwelling-house of God.

Such thinking pervaded through the development of criminal law and led to all manner of beautifully argued High Court decisions. Such discussion became facetiously known as legal fiction and included arguments such as whether a tent could be a dwelling-house or whether movable structures like caravans and houseboats, or even flats, were dwelling-houses. A building could be considered a dwelling-house even if no one lived in it at the time, but the main point of the crime, when I joined the police force, was that it could only occur between the hours of 9 pm and 6 am, the period between those times being regarded as "night".

Because burglary was regarded so seriously, night-duty constables paid great attention to the likelihood of burglars being abroad on their beats, and a thorough knowledge of the ingredients of the crime was drummed into us; we had to recognise a burglar when we saw one, not because of his striped sweater and bag of swag, but because of his ability to commit acts which were within the wording of the legal definition of burglary. The legal definition was completely changed by the Theft Act 1968, but I can still recall the old one which created such gorgeous decisions in court.

It was provided by Section 25 of the Larceny Act 1916 and read as follows:

"Every person who in the night,

(i)   breaks and enters the dwelling-house of another with intent to commit any felony therein;

or

(ii) breaks out of the dwelling-house of another having

(a)   entered the said dwelling-house with intent to commit any felony therein;

(b)   having committed any felony in the said dwelling-house shall be guilty of felony called burglary and on conviction thereof liable to imprisonment for life."

That definition was instilled into us at Training School so we would never forget it; and it was an interesting crime to study. There was a very helpful mnemonic which helped us to learn its provisions. It was: IN BED.

We learned the provisions of the crime by writing those initial letters in this manner:

I — Intent.

Intent to commit any felony therein.

N — Night.

Must be committed at night, i.e., between 9 pm and 6 am.

B — Breaking.

There must be a breaking, either constructive or actual. Mere entry without a breaking does not constitute burglary.

E — Entry.

The house has to be entered either by inserting some part of the body like a hand or an instrument like a hook on a stick.

D — Dwelling-house.

It had to be a dwelling-house of another, not a shop, factory, school, church or other building. These are all catered for in other sections of the Larceny Act 1916. Houses broken into during the daytime are separate offences.

That, then, was burglary as learned by young constables until 1968 and as we patrolled our beats during those long night-hours we were always alert for the possibility of houses being burgled or were seeking incidents which would exercise the practical side of our instruction.

For example, did "breaking" include climbing down a chimney, or was the lifting of a cellar-flap within that meaning? In one case the burglar got struck in a chimney because it was of inadequate proportions and he had to be pulled clear. Certainly entry via a chimney was "entry" for burglaries, but could it, in all honesty, be regarded as a "break-in"?

If a person smashed a window in order to climb in, that is *actual breaking,* but the legal fiction of criminal law was stretched to its limit by calling some entries *constructive breaking.* For example, if our enterprising burglar tricked his way into a house or bullied his way in and thus got *someone else* to open the doors and break the continuity of the building, that was known as constructive breaking. We were told that this properly fell within the maxim "*qui facit per alium facit per se*", which was probably very important. But suppose the criminal climbed through a window that had not been glazed or simply opened a door which was not locked? And suppose he broke into a cupboard?

These and many more imponderables exercised our minds at Training School and provided marvellous ammunition for examination questions. Having studied all aspects of the crime and learned the value of all the words in the definition we were presented with baffling questions — we were asked about evil-doers who broke into houses with an intent to rest their weary limbs and not commit felonious deeds therein. Were they burglars? Should we consider some other form of nocturnal illegality? One enterprising felon said he'd entered a house at night to see the ghosts which were said to haunt it while another said he'd entered to attack a horse. The latter raised the question of whether a stable is a dwelling-house. It might be if it is *attached* to a dwelling-house . . . but the fellow did not intend to kill the horse but merely to stop it winning a race. Is that felony? And suppose a boy broke into a house to wind up all the clocks?

Thus our mental gymnastics continued in the shape of examination questions and finally, having studied past centuries of case law, we were cast out to apprehend real burglars.

In truth they were very few. If such offences did occur, they were usually recorded as "housebreaking" because it is not easy to prove beyond all doubt that the crime had been committed during the night. Apart from making the police station statistics less alarming by revealing a spate of illegal nocturnal "enterings" at the houses of others it was far easier to prove that a housebreaker had paid a visit. For example, if a householder woke up at 6.05 am to find his house had been broken into during the night, how could he prove it had occurred before 6 am? Not a chance! It might have happened at 6.02 am, so it was recorded as housebreaking, an infinitely less serious breach of the law. By this method, the police prevented many burglaries.

On my rural beat at Aidensfield I could ponder upon Gilbert and Sullivan's burglars and cut-throats, gurgling brooks and merry village chimes, but I did wonder if such evil-doers ever paid visits to my beat. The first indication that they did visit me came one lovely summer evening.

I was patrolling in Eltering, performing one of my periodic night-shifts in the small market town and made my midnight point outside the post office. It was known to the telephone operators who occupied the first floor that policemen stood outside that kiosk at approximately midnight. Sometimes, if a friendly operator was on duty, we would be invited in for a cup of tea, always taking care to dodge the sergeant.

On such an evening, therefore, I was studiously loitering beside the silent kiosk when the upper-floor window opened, and a man's head appeared, framed in the light.

"Officer," he said, not recognising me as a local police-man. "There's burglars, I think."

"Burglars!" Horror made little mice with chilly feet run up and down my spine. "Where?"

"Either in the Youth Hostel or at the Youth Club," he said. "I'm not sure which."

My mind rattled off the definition. A youth hostel could be a dwelling-house but a youth club? Could that be classi-fied as a store? School? Warehouse? Or even a dwelling-house if someone lived on the premises?

"Why can't you be sure?" I asked from below.

"They've a party line," he said. "They've knocked the telephone off the hook and I can hear them — they're talk-ing, and I've heard money rattling."

"And you don't know which place it is?"

"No," he said, and at that moment Sergeant Bairstow appeared adventitiously from the shadows.

"Trouble, Nicholas?" he asked.

"Burglars, Sergeant," and I gave a brief account of my puzzling conversation with the telephone operator who still dangled from the upper window waiting for instant action from us.

"We can't ring them to find out, can we?" He rubbed his chin.

"No, Sergeant," I agreed with this diagnosis.

"So it's either the Youth Club or the Youth Hostel," he said, still rubbing his chin. "And they're still inside, eh? This will be great, Nicholas, if we catch 'em red-handed. Right, we'll investigate," and he turned his eyes heavenwards. The operator had, in the meantime, vanished inside, but returned to announce, "They're still there, and they're smashing something open. I can hear them."

"Thanks, we're off to attend to it. Don't alarm them."

Twenty yards farther along the road Sergeant Bairstow halted and it is prudent to recall that this was long before the days when policemen had radio sets and motorcars. Our assets were two feet each, and our problem was that the two buildings in question were at least a mile from each other.

"We'll check the Youth Club first, together. It's the most likely to be done," he advised.

The decision made, we hurried along the narrow streets to the building which housed the Youth Club. It had once been a school and was perched on a patch of land adjoining the river which twisted through Eltering. It was a tall building of Victorian bricks and boasted a lot of attics, staircases, roof windows and hidden corners. It was surrounded on three sides by a high brick wall inside which was an area once used as a playground. Now it was marked with lines for a multitude of ball-games. The fourth side abutted the river from which entrance on foot was impossible.

If the burglars were in here how had they entered?

The door into the yard was locked, so I had to climb over the wall. As it was over ten feet high I had to get a "leg-up" from Sergeant Bairstow, but in no time I was perched on top and faced a long drop into the yard beneath. I lowered myself gently and dropped the final feet, striking the concrete well below street level. I was now alone in the enclosed area and moved gently across the yard, seeking indications of felonious persons. I tried the two doors which led into the buildings — there was not a sign of a break-in. The place was in darkness and was secure. I shone my torch on all the windows — all were locked and not one was broken.

Somehow Charlie Bairstow had clambered to the top of the wall and sat astride it, shining his torch on to all the roof windows, the roof lights and other likely places of entry. Nothing. It seemed this place was secure.

"I'll check the river side," I said. This meant inching my way along the side of the premises through a narrow alley full of old bottles, leaves and tins until I found myself peering over a high wall above the river. And there, moored to the wall, was a small rowing-boat. It was empty and parked on a patch of thick black mud.

My heart began to thump. They *were* here, inside, right now. If we could surround the building we'd get them!

I shone my torch along the wall and found a likely place of entry — a window set high in the riverside wall. I could just see it if I stood precariously on the wall, hanging on to a tree and leaning out across the exposed mud. But that window was not broken, nor was it open. I could even see the catch — it was locked. Maybe they'd got inside and closed the window to conceal their presence?

I ran back to Sergeant Bairstow and whispered to him.

"There's a rowing-boat down there," I said. "It's tucked into the bank just below a window, but the window is locked."

"I'm coming down," and he lowered himself gingerly into the yard. After I had showed him the stationary vessel, we both checked every inch of that building and found not a solitary indication of felonious entry. Wherever possible we shone our lights through ground-floor windows but never saw any indication of villainy.

"That boat's got nothing to do with it," he announced. "I'm sure of that. It'll be a club boat, a privately-owned one even. Nothing to worry about."

"Let's get the key-holder out," I suggested, wondering how we were going to climb out of the yard. The wall was far too high.

"Ring the office from the kiosk up the street," he said. "Tell them to get the key-holder out and come here as fast as possible. Meanwhile, we'll check the Youth Hostel. I'm convinced the burglars aren't here."

In spite of the boat I had to agree. We managed to climb out of the yard by teetering along the riverside wall and into the back garden of a neighbouring house. From there we tiptoed into the street via the garden path. Before leaving, we made a final check but came away satisfied that not a solitary window or door had been burgled. That Youth Club was as safe as Fort Knox.

"It's a queer job," he said for no apparent reason as we turned for a final look at the deserted building. I felt it was offering us a challenge; was the felon inside, laughing at us? If he was, he must have gone through the roof.

"Come along," Charlie Bairstow said. "Youth Hostel next. I wonder if that telephone operator was imagining things?"

In a very isolated position, the Youth Hostel was known to have cash on the premises, in addition to food and drink. It presented a very likely target, so we hurried about our business. It stood near the castle, about a mile out of town and this meant a long, panting hike through the streets. With Sergeant Bairstow puffing and panting, we both climbed through narrow alleys to the long, low-roofed building. It had once been a row of miners' homes and had long since been converted into a youth hostel of considerable charm.

It was in total darkness. Like the Youth Club it was difficult for two of us to surround it, so we each went a different way, each creeping around the peaceful spot. We examined doors, windows and other points of possible entry. I found nothing insecure and met Sergeant Bairstow heading towards me.

"Nothing, Sergeant. It looks secure."

"So does my half," he said. "Test mine, and I'll do yours."

And so both of us concluded a complete tour of the Youth Hostel without finding any insecurities. There was no trace of felonious entry. Our next task, to be completely certain, was to rouse the warden.

She was a fierce lady of indeterminate age and sex, but, considering we knocked her from her slumbers about one o'clock in the morning, she was surprisingly affable. When she had learned of our business we were invited inside; there we searched the office and examined the entire building, including the safe. And the telephone was still on its stand. This place hadn't been burgled. So it must be the Youth Club.

We declined her cup of tea saying our inquiry had taken a turn for the urgent and hurried back into town. My legs were aching after the variety of exercises they had recently endured, and Sergeant Bairstow was panting like "a broken winded gallower", as we say in North Yorkshire. Before long, we were back at the dark and brooding Youth Club. The key-holder hadn't arrived yet.

"I'll check again," so I ventured down the neighbouring garden path and along the wall which bordered the river. And I noticed the boat had vanished!

"Sarge!" I called, ignoring the need for caution. "Sarge, here!"

He came panting to the wall top and I worried momentarily for his safety as I pointed to the vacant space.

"That boat's gone," I said stupidly.

"We've missed 'em," he sounded very sad. "You know, Nicholas, I've never caught a breaker red-handed in my whole career. And I could have tonight, eh? And they were there all the bloody time . . . How did they get in? It must have been a duplicate key job."

As we discussed that and other possibilities I heard the sound of a large key in the lock of the gate which led into the yard, and I went with lighted torch to greet the key-holder. Sergeant Bairstow followed. A small meek man wearing a sweater and old slacks entered and blinked as our lights picked out his pale face.

"I'm Sergeant Bairstow," said Charlie.

"Mr Woolley," he said. "Youth Leader. They said it might be burglars."

"We think so," and the sergeant outlined the story. Nervously Mr Woolley approached one of the doors and inserted his key. It opened with a slight squeak and he stood back to let us in. I entered, followed by a tired Sergeant Bairstow, while Mr Woolley came a shaky third, putting on the lights. He led us to the office — sure enough, the telephone had been knocked from its stand and was still dangling at the end of its wire. The desk drawer had been forced and all the cash taken, together with other valuables like drink, cigarettes and sweets. It had been a thorough raid.

Mr Woolley sank to the floor and sighed heavily while Bairstow cried, "God! We'll cop it for this . . . We could have had them. I could have caught them . . ."

I was curious to know how they'd got in and began a tour of the brightly lit place, seeking the point of entry. And I found it. I found a staircase which led from the centre of the club and twisted high towards other floors, four flights in all. Each landing had a tiny window and one of those had been broken; entry had been via this point, and I realised it was impossible to see it from ground level. It opened across a hollow in the roof and was totally invisible from below.

I wondered how they'd reached that point from the boat for there was no drainpipe at that side of the building. They must have been human flies.

The outcome of our *faux pas* was that the CID were called in. They came to fingerprint the place, including the telephone, which was eventually replaced on its stand. A check by Mr Woolley showed that some £32 had been stolen, in addition to food and drinks worth about £9. I told the detective sergeant about the boat and he smiled, saying, "Crafty sods, eh? Coming in boat? Can you describe it, Nick?"

"Just a small rowing-boat," I said. I hadn't noticed its colour or anything else about it except that it was small, perhaps a two-seater. I did remember seeing a small quantity of water in its bottom and told him that.

"We'll run a check on all boats," he promised.

And so we adjourned. We searched the town for signs of burglars wandering about, and I checked all the riverside boats to see if I recognised the one they'd used. I didn't. Finally I went to bed, tired and upset that we'd missed the villains. When I came on duty the following night I found a note from the detective sergeant. It simply said, "Check the Youth Club again — we're still interested in that boat."

I wondered if this indicated information that they might return? CID intelligence must have unearthed some reliable gen. I might catch them red-handed this time! Accordingly, I journeyed to Eltering and made it my business to check the Youth Club once more, very, very thoroughly. I tiptoed through the neighbour's garden as before and once again crept along the riverside wall.

My heart leapt!

It was there. Lying low in the water was the boat in exactly the same position as last night, and my heart was beating so violently that I felt it would disturb the burglars. I then realised that if the burglars *were* expected, the CID would have arranged a reception party.

They were probably inside too, waiting . . .

I shone my torch on the boat. It was a battered old craft now that I began to examine it more carefully. And that damp patch in the middle . . . it was mud! Just like the surrounding mud of the river bed, now exposed. It had a massive hole in the bottom. It was derelict. It could never float in a million years and couldn't have sailed anywhere this century!

And high tide was coming in . . .

Even this far inland the river was tidal and with a sinking heart I realised what had happened. In the time we'd been at the Youth Hostel, the water had risen a few inches, sufficient to cover the wrecked boat.

So they hadn't burgled by boat.

They must have simply climbed over the wall, shinned up a drainpipe and broken in through that lofty hidden window. And it wasn't a dwelling-house either, so it couldn't be classed as burglary.

We wrote it down as office-breaking, but the typist misspelt it as officer-creaking. Maybe it wasn't a mistake?

In very erudite terms the detective sergeant told me to be more careful with my observations in the future and Sergeant Bairstow was instructed to keep a tight eye on local towns and villages at night. I knew the senior ranks weren't very happy about our detection rate and did not want a repeat of the Youth Club fiasco. Sergeant Bairstow considered it his duty to teach the constables under his wing something of crime prevention techniques. He taught me how to walk in the shadows, to check suspicious vehicles, to note the movements of suspicious people and to record a host of other minutiae, any one of which could be instrumental in detecting a crime.

Charlie Bairstow became very burglar-conscious and persuaded the Crime Prevention Department to play its part. Together we advised shopkeepers and householders about leaving windows ajar, especially those on the ground floor, and we reminded them not to leave newspapers protruding from letterboxes or allow full milk bottles to remain on the doorsteps for days. We described them all as invitations to burglars.

One of Sergeant Bairstow's pet themes was "keys hanging on string". If he had a favourite "don't", this was it. He would preach the gospel at schools and Women's Institutes for it was a very common practice by householders to leave the door key hanging on a piece of string behind the letter-box. How easy it is for the burgling gentleman to locate and use; Sergeant Bairstow failed to understand why intelligent people left their keys for burglars in this fashion. Lots did it, and lots got burgled. It was his antagonism to this practice that caused us a slight problem one night.

I was walking down Partridge Hill in Eltering intent on checking an office block at the bottom when I espied Sergeant Bairstow waiting for me. He stood beneath a lamp standard and smiled warmly as I approached.

"All correct, Sergeant," I assured him.

"You've not checked those offices yet?"

"They're next on my list, Sergeant."

"Then tell me what you see wrong, Nicholas."

I checked the door at the entrance and it was locked. All the ground-floor windows were also locked. The place seemed impregnable. Then I recalled his current obsession about keys on string and glanced at the front door. The letterbox was standing open; in fact, it was non-existent and in its place was a large, oblong hole through which letters were pushed. It was high in the door in a vertical position, like a large figure "1" in the centre panel. And behind I could see a piece of string. I smiled.

"This, Sergeant?"

"Well done, lad. Good observation, you know. Yes, now that is a foolish example, isn't it? We just lift out the string . . ." and he hooked his forefinger behind it and hauled about three feet out. A Yale key dangled from the end. Smiling at the success of this practical tutorial, he said, "and we fit it into the lock."

Sure enough it worked. The key was clearly shared by all the users of the premises for the door swung open. We went inside to check that burglars had not done likewise. The interior boasted half a dozen locked doors, and upstairs was a similar arrangement. These doors led into small offices rented from the owner of the building, and every office was secure. None the less, he had a valid point. A breaker-in could lurk inside, securely hidden from the outside world, as he carried out a furtive raid on one of the offices.

When we had been right round the internal route we returned to the front door. He paused and said, "We'll remove it, for safety," and with no more ado Sergeant Bairstow untied the string from its hook above the letterbox and said, "We'll fix it to the bottom."

A large screw protruded at the bottom end of the letterbox gap, and he carefully tied the string to it, saying, "This'll prevent it being noticed so easily." He left the key dangling inside the door, but its lifeline was now safely concealed from the outside world. We left, and I slammed the door. The office block was now secure.

I was about three strides away when I realised with horror what we'd done.

"Sergeant," I called, halting abruptly.

"Yes?"

"They can't get in now, can they?"

"They can, they know where the key is. The burglars don't."

"But they can't reach it. It's hanging *below* the letterbox and it's impossible to put a hand through that small gap to get hold of the string."

He stood in silence for a few moments and then said, "Oh, bloody hell!"

We examined the door. Sure enough, the gap was there but it was far too small to accommodate anyone's fist, let alone a policeman's. No one could reach that office key. I visualised lots of irate office workers tomorrow morning, all hammering on their door or ringing the Superintendent to complain about interfering policemen. Try as we might we could not reach that string.

"Oh, bloody hell!" he said again. "What can we do?"

"We need a bit of wire," I suggested. "A stiff bit to hook it out."

"I know where we can find some."

He led off at a fast trot and we were soon tramping around the backyard of an electrical contractor's premises where scrap of all kinds abounded. His torch eventually located a length of thick wire about eighteen inches long. It was pliable enough to bend yet strong enough to remain in any selected shape.

Marching triumphantly through the town with this up his sleeve he and I returned to the door. I now wondered if we were committing a crime of "possessing housebreaking implements by night". The wording of the offence did qualify it by adding "without lawful excuse", and I wondered if ours was a lawful excuse? It was too late to worry about our actions because Sergeant Bairstow was already at the door asking me to stand guard in case anyone came. I had to whistle if someone approached.

From my vantage point I saw him shape the piece of wire into a long, straight piece with a large, angled hook at the bottom and a type of handle at the top. Carefully he inserted his improvised key retrieval device into the narrow letterbox. He missed. He cursed. He must have missed several times and he cursed several times before he asked me if I could help as my fingers were probably more nimble than his. I did. I inserted the hooked wire and played around with it inside the door, groping for the elusive length of string. I must admit it took a lot of finding and I missed it several times. Then I felt it. The key moved and rattled lightly against the timbers of the door and I gently lifted my piece of wire. And out it came. Sergeant Bairstow was delighted. He proudly opened the door and we restored the key to its former place.

He wasn't happy about the key so visibly hanging behind the open letterbox but felt there was little he could do that night. He'd speak to the office workers at a later date.

"Some folks deserve to be burgled," he said as he strode away.

CHAPTER NINE

Tell him his pranks have been too broad to bear with.
WILLIAM SHAKESPEARE — *Hamlet*

The solitary policeman who patrols the streets and lanes at night regularly finds himself with the time and the opportunity to contemplate. He finds himself thinking about the meaning of life and there are many sage sayings which adequately illustrate his mental attitude during those long, silent hours. The poets have endeavoured to capture the character of night and have produced fine phrases like "ships that pass in the night" or "the shades of night which fell so fast". Policemen, on the other hand, are much more practical and tend to consider "nights that are lang and mirk" or "long, long wintry nights" or the "longest night in all the year". If policemen do lean towards poetry, they consider themselves "sentries of the shadowy night" or even "sons of the sable night".

It may be possible to fill a book with such quotations but police officers are not keen on ratiocinated quotations unless they are created by themselves. Although night-duty does give time for the constable to produce words of wisdom this seldom happens. Instead, the quiet times breed mischief.

One passable form of activity is to play jokes upon one's colleagues. One advantage of this is that it is possible to use the whole district as a playground, but a distinct disadvantage is that one becomes so involved and excited that one forgets that the public sometimes suffer from a lack of sleep and peer out of their windows. Another important factor is that sergeants, inspectors and even superintendents have a nasty habit of creeping up on the frolicking policemen and this leads to all kinds of disciplinary trouble.

In general, though, the pranks are harmless. One very popular prank was to creep around the police officers' bicycles, which were parked all night outside the station, and remove their saddles. These were concealed, and the morning witnessed several poor bobbies, tired after their night patrols, cycling home in curious positions, not daring to sit on the dangerously protruding seat-pillars. By the next night the seats had returned. Another trick was to remove one pedal so that the constable had to cycle home by using only one leg. Alternative caps would be switched on the hat rack so that it was a most difficult job to find one's own headpiece. All good, harmless fun.

In addition to these internal pranks many tricks were played in the streets. It was the misfortune of most new constables to be the victim of such pranks, but at a small station like Aidensfield or Ashfordly it was very unlikely that I would become a victim because our night-duty stints were often solitary affairs. None the less, the possibility always remained, particularly when patrolling the streets of nearby Eltering or Strensford. When working in a strange area one had always to be alert to such possibilities and I bore this in mind when working at those stations.

I remember one poor constable, newly arrived from the City of London. At the tender age of twenty he had only a few months' service in that Force and had transferred to the north to be near his fiancée. He was given the task of patrolling a beat in Eltering, and had the misfortune to encounter Ben and Ron, the two traffic terrors. Over one of our mid-shift breakfasts they casually mentioned that it was the duty of the town night-shift man to arouse the local keeper of the dogs' home. They told that constable that the keeper liked to be up at five o'clock in the morning in order to exercise and feed all the inmates. Because he was notoriously bad at getting out of bed, he had left a standing request for the night-duty policemen to rouse him at five. The police had agreed because his father was a magistrate in York.

That is what they told the poor young constable. It was, of course, a load of rubbish. Even worse was their recommended method of rousing him. These merrymaking constables coolly told the youngster that the only way to rouse the sleepy keeper was to kick and hammer loudly on his door for a full five minutes. They carefully told him which door to use.

And so the diligent youngster had gone about this duty. The result was that the entire town was roused by the continued and irate barking of dozens of stray dogs, an action which did arouse the puzzled keeper.

Another prank was perpetrated by a sergeant who dressed as a road sweeper and cleaned the streets in the early hours of the morning. He performed his dramatic role whenever a new constable was patrolling, and it was a comparatively simple operation. He borrowed a barrow and broom from the Highways Depot and, dressed like a tramp, swept the town at 3 am or thereabouts. He did this to test the reaction of the constable concerned. But what does a constable do when he sees a road sweeper at work so early?

Sergeants, I suppose, are just as guilty as their men for playing tricks on one another or upon their subordinates, although it must be said that many of these were done with valid reasons. For example, many night-shifts tolerate one constable who cannot remain awake, especially when on office-duty. Tricks were played on him in an attempt to keep him awake.

One of the funniest of this kind involved my pal Dave at Brantsford, who nodded off in the middle of a long report about an alleged case of careless driving. I had been on night patrol with Sergeant Bairstow and he decided to call at Brantsford Police Office on a routine visit. Dave was on duty. The lights were on and we made no pretence about being silent. It would be around five o'clock in the morning.

Inside we found Dave fast asleep. He was sitting at the typewriter with his elbow on the desk and his head resting on his upright hand, fast asleep. More amazing, there was a cup of cold tea dangling from his upright hand, the handle hooked upon one of his fingers. The cup was about half full and somehow his hands supported both a cup and his head. The unfinished report was in the typewriter.

"Look at that!" grinned Sergeant Bairstow. "It's bloody amazing — he's out like a light."

"Shall I wake him?" I asked.

"Not yet," he grinned. And Sergeant Bairstow crept into the office and climbed onto a chair. He carefully opened the face of the wall clock and moved the pointers forward from 5 to 7.30. The he beckoned me to stand where I was. He joined me.

For a moment he watched the snoozing Dave and his amazing cup of tea, then shouted, "Morning, PC Watts."

Dave jerked into instant life. His tousled head shook into wakefulness as he struggled to open his eyes and the cup now jolted so much that he poured its contents all over the blotting-pad.

"Sorry," he apologised. "You surprised me."

"Is that important?" asked Bairstow, indicating the unfinished report.

"I'm going on holiday, Sergeant, when I finish at six, and wanted it done by then."

"Six?" a puzzled expression appeared on Bairstow's face and I realised he was no mean actor.

"Nights," Dave replied in all innocence. "I'm on nights — I finish at six, Sarge, and we're going straight off in the car. We've a ferry to catch at Hull . . ."

"I thought you were on Early Turn," said Sergeant Bairstow, frowning and looking at his watch.

This action caused Dave to turn and look at the clock behind him, and he leapt from the chair. "Half past seven!" he cried. "Bloody hell, I should be driving through York now . . ."

"York?"

"Yes, on the way to Hull . . . I was supposed to be on the road by half six . . . bloody hell . . ."

And he began ripping out his unfinished report, rushing round the office, tidying up and generally generating something of a whirlwind as we stood and watched. He mopped up his spilt tea and I could see he was terribly agitated.

I wondered what the sergeant would do next. He did nothing.

"Sorry, Sarge," cried Dave, almost running out of the office with his hat on the back of his head and his jacket open. "Thanks, Sarge, I mean . . ."

And Charlie Bairstow allowed him to leave. The last I saw of Dave that morning was his flying figure as he tore from the police station to rouse his family. Only then would he realise what had really happened.

The truth was that Sergeant Bairstow had used this method to give him an hour off duty before going on holiday. It was also a reminder that one should not fall asleep on duty, and I knew Dave would always remember this lesson.

"Come along, Nicholas, it will be six o'clock by the time we return."

A lot of pranks were undertaken to relieve the crushing boredom, but others were perpetrated to teach less friendly policemen a lesson. It must be said that every police station, large or small, has its own rotten egg. He could be too keen on prosecuting the public, too hard on kids, or simply a misfit among his fellow officers. Such policemen are unpopular, even among policemen.

There are many kinds of unpopular cops — it might be a youngster from an upper-class background who thinks himself superior to his colleagues — it might be a brainbox who has passed all his exams and is good at academic subjects but hopeless at practical policing, or it might be a keen officer who books every possible defaulter for the most trivial offences. Whatever their faults, disliked officers can be treated with considerable contempt by their colleagues.

Such a fellow arrived at Eltering a few months after I was posted to Aidensfield. He was a tall, Nordic-looking character with high cheekbones and wavy blond hair. He considered himself God's answer to Romeo and, worse still, he came from the south. This accident of birth immediately segregated him from the Yorkshiremen about him. It must be said, however, that his southern nativity alone did not cause any real rift because Yorkshiremen are kind enough to such unfortunates to attempt a programme of conversion. During this intensive course the incomer would be taught the ways of Yorkshire folk and would begin to understand their wiles. If such incomers were wise, they would accept the lessons or respect the advice given. If they were stupid, they would attempt to outwit the Yorkshiremen.

This particular constable, whose name was Sean O'Malley and who looked nothing like an Irishman, was none the less christened "Paddy" on the day he arrived. His first action was to promptly let everyone know he resented this name because he wasn't Irish. "Sean" was acceptable, he said, nothing more, nothing less. So Sean it was to his face, and Snooty or Paddy behind his back.

His attitude soon upset the local constables and indeed the populace. The local police were upset because he scathingly compared the tiny market town of Eltering with the busy metropolis of London, and he upset the residents by coldly reporting them for all manner of curious offences like tethering mules on the highway, shaking mats before 8 am, having shop-blinds less than eight feet above the footpath, fixing flowerpots on window-ledges without securing them, repairing cars in the street and many similar wrongs. He seemed to revel in unearthing the most unrealistic laws to enforce.

This made him less than popular with the sergeants who disliked having to submit his reports for consideration by their superiors. It alienated him from his superiors because they had to make decisions whether or not to prosecute these startling illegalities. He once set about proving that a local tramp was an incorrigible rogue by using the full weight of the Vagrancy Act 1824, and even tried to prosecute a fairground fortune-teller for being a fraudulent medium. He had a passion for inspecting old motor vehicles in the hope he would find horrific crimes created by flapping mudguards, ineffective warning instruments, mobile cranes with wheels too large, agricultural tractors used for purposes not connected with agriculture, rakish cars bearing dangerous mascots, trailers without the requisite number of attendants, solo motorcycles towing trailers and a multitude of parking positions which he believed were causing unnecessary obstructions.

The snag was that all the farmers ran old bangers. These unclean vehicles would carry corn, corpses, sheep, pigs and hens, vegetable produce and sometimes even people. It was not prudent to ask whether these were "social, domestic and pleasure" purposes, nor was it deemed wise to ask if the car was taxed only for private use. Sean's activities meant that every trip into town was a financial hazard because of a possible court appearance, so people did not venture into Eltering if he was likely to be on duty. As a result the economic future of Eltering, especially on market day, was threatened.

The result was that Snooty Paddy believed he had cleaned up the town. Gone was the huge number of horrendous offences which had threatened the security of the town before his arrival. Now there was a marketplace peopled by law-abiding citizens and a handful of cars with no faults. All the faulty ones stayed at home, or else went to Harrowby market.

The sergeants spoke to this man in an effort to encourage him to take a more realistic view of life and a more reasonable approach to the public. But their efforts failed. Sean knew his law and it was his duty to enforce that law. There would be no discrimination, no favouritism, no slacking, no question of preferential treatment. If an offence was committed, that offence would be reported by him for summons.

His activities around the undersides of cars, lorries and buses caused him to be known as Gravel Knees, a derisory nickname which he failed to discover.

The problem facing his supervisory officers was how to cure him of his disease. Doing one's job correctly in the police service is never easy for there is always that element of society who feel they have been badly treated or have suffered some injustice. Men like Gravel Knees believe they are treating everyone alike and that their actions do not lead to injustice. In truth, they are a menace to society. To rigidly enforce every rule, law and order down to its full stops and commas, is stupidity at its very worst and persecution at its best.

I am reminded of the old saying, "Rules are made for the obedience of fools and the guidance of wise men", and most police officers feel this is a good guide to sensible law enforcement. Gravel Knees was a fool and discussions about him were held in high places, even in very high places. We learned he had left the Metropolitan Police due to antagonism from senior officers. Down there, it seems, he had enforced the Metropolitan Police Act with such fervour that he undid years of good crime detection work by other officers. Men, like detectives, rely on the public for freely given crime-busting information and spend years building up relationships. Good informants were getting booked by Gravel Knees for various social evils like getting drunk or quitting their cars without switching off the engine, and thereafter they refused to cooperate in the fight against serious crime.

If Gravel Knees was rigid in his attitude towards the law, he was equally rigid in the application of his duty. If the sergeant told him to patrol the town and personally try every doorknob, he would do exactly that without any question. An order was an order. He did not question authority of any kind, being firmly in the belief that those who issued orders had Guidance From Above, and that there were many sound reasons for the orders in question. The man was almost an automaton.

His peculiar attitude to life set us talking one night. I was on duty, patrolling my beat in the little Ford Anglia and halted at Eltering for my morning break at 2 am. Gravel Knees was assigned to Eltering town that same night. At our mid-shift meal break was Vesuvius from Malton, the two Road Traffic lads, Ben and Ron, Sergeant Bairstow, Gravel Knees and myself. It made a cosy gathering, all of us sitting in the tiny office with mugs of tea and sandwiches. We chattered like pals of many years' standing, such is the camaraderie of the police service.

During our discussion the question of blind obedience arose, and Ron skilfully manoeuvred the subject to the testing of doorknobs.

"I maintain that not every doorknob should be checked," he pontificated. "I mean, there are places that no one in his right mind is going to enter unlawfully, so why check them?"

"I disagree," said Sergeant Bairstow. I now knew him well enough to spot a very cheeky gleam in his eye. "Every door should be checked. If our orders say we must check every door, then that's what must be done. Orders are not compiled without good reason, Ron. They're often the product of past experiences."

"The point I'm making," returned Ron, "is that common sense must be used in the interpretation of orders. I mean . . . Let's see . . ." and he thought for a few moments. "Suppose you haven't checked something like the monumental mason's backyard — it's full of half completed tombstones and slabs bearing inscriptions. Who's going to pinch anything from there, I ask you? So why worry about checking it for security?"

"Go on, what's your point?" I wondered if he and Charlie Bairstow had pre-arranged this little chat. It had the hallmarks of a lead-in to something else.

"Okay. My point is this. I am patrolling my beat and I am very aware that I have not checked that gate. The yard might be open. It is a few minutes to knocking-off time. If I go and check that yard, I will be half-an-hour late into the office, and this can cause concern to the office staff and to my senior officers. They may think I've been attacked or something. So I omit to check the yard and return to the office on time. I think I've made the right decision, and I base that on the grounds that a check of such an establishment is not justified in those circumstances."

"I disagree," came in Gravel Knees. "If you did that under the circumstances you describe you would be disobeying a lawful order. There is no excuse for that, no excuse at all."

"Balls!" said Ron, scornfully.

The conversation continued in this vein until it was time to leave, and I commenced the second half of my tour of duty, thinking over Ron's discussion with Sergeant Bairstow. It had been a strange conversation, I decided, and I wondered why they had chosen to talk about tombstones and graveyards. I got the answer the following night.

We were all in the same police station at the same time. Some had come in early for their meal break and the argument was still raging. Gravel Knees was at the centre of it, receiving what we call a "lug-hole bashing" from the others. I must say he held his ground well, and all his arguments appeared to be backed by a close study of the rules. In that sense he was unshakeable.

Having eaten, Vesuvius left early to continue his patrol and within five minutes Sergeant Bairstow also left. Ron and Ben remained with me and Sean O'Malley, alias Gravel Knees. The tempo of the discussion subsided.

Ron and Ben kept it alive, but only just, saying how terrible it would be if every motoring law was strictly enforced. England would become a police state, Ron reckoned, but O'Malley could not see this. He maintained that rules were for a purpose and they must be enforced if that purpose was to be achieved for the good of society.

Precisely at the end of his forty-five minutes' meal break, Gravel Knees left the office. I was now alone with Ben and Ron.

"I hope you won't grow into that kind of copper, Nick," said Ron. "Rules, rules, rules . . . people like him are incapable of using their initiative."

"He'll grow out of it," I said, not being able to think of anything more apt at the time.

"He won't," Ben swore. "Blokes like him are with us forever."

"He's in for a shock tonight," said Ron, smiling at me.

"Shock?" I puzzled.

"They've set him up for a little test," said Ron. "It'll either make him or break him. Tonight he will decide whether every rule needs to be rigidly enforced, or he will decide that, on occasions, rules can be relaxed or ignored, depending upon prevailing circumstances."

"How?" I asked, full of interest.

This is what occurred.

The prime movers in this escapade were Sergeant Bairstow and Vesuvius, and it seems that the basic idea had come from Vesuvius. One of the lock-up properties on O'Malley's beat that night was the mortuary, and Vesuvius knew that it contained a corpse. This was not unusual because that mortuary often had overnight guests and one of the keys was retained at the police station. The building was sometimes checked by the officer on night patrol and on several occasions new or inexperienced constables had terrified themselves by shining their torches on to handsome bodies laid out for further attention.

Vesuvius considered that O'Malley should be put to the test and he selected the mortuary and its current occupant for the job. Sergeant Bairstow had agreed to this course of action.

Knowing how rigidly O'Malley worked they reckoned he would leave his meal break at 2.30 am, patrol the town centre for some forty-five minutes and then head for the mortuary, which was behind a small chapel. His estimated time of arrival was 3.20 am on a cool, autumn morning.

Such was Vesuvius' dedication to the task in hand that he entered the mortuary at 2.30 and sat in the clinically cold place for three-quarters of an hour with his right hand immersed in a bucket of icy water. This had the effect of reducing the temperature of that hand almost to freezing point, but he endured this discomfort for the sake of Eltering town.

He positioned himself behind the inner door and left the outer door unlocked. The theory was that O'Malley would check it at 3.20 am or thereabouts, find it insecure and walk in. If he obeyed the dictates of his conscience he would enter the mortuary to make a thorough check. Vesuvius was relying on that.

Inside, therefore, Vesuvius waited behind one of the inner swing-doors and on the stone slab immediately inside was the corpse of an old gentleman, emaciated and naked. Sergeant Bairstow was crouched at the far side of the corpse, and a close observer would have noticed a broom in his hand. The head of the broom was beneath the shoulders of the dear departed as he lay upon the slab. His frail old head dangled over the end with its eyes uppermost.

Vesuvius waited with his right hand in the bucket of icy water as the long minutes ticked by. In the dim light which filtered into the place from the town outside the stark white corpse could be seen but nothing else. The place was as still as death; there was not a sound.

"Any sign of him?" asked Sergeant Bairstow in a hoarse whisper.

"Nothing," replied Vesuvius.

3.20 came and went. And then there were sounds outside. A heavy, measured tread could be heard upon the flagged path, and Vesuvius whispered, "He's here, Sarge!"

Only now did he remove his hand from the water and dry it on a towel he had borrowed, tossing it into the corner behind the door. The outer door rattled as someone tested the knob. The door opened, and they heard the faintest of squeaks as it admitted the visitor. Vesuvius smiled to himself. Bairstow whispered, "Ready?"

Then the inner door creaked as the handle turned slowly. The knob rattled very faintly as it opened inwards, to the left. Behind the other inner door, the one on the right, there waited Vesuvius of the Icy Hand.

A torch was clicked on. The sombre place was filled with light as the figure stepped forward and, at that precise moment, Vesuvius reached from the shadows with his horrible hand to seize the hand of the visitor and draw him into the mortuary. As that icy cold and damp hand seized the other, the corpse groaned, or so it seemed, and slowly began to sit upright, its pale thin body indistinct in the gloom away from the shaking torch.

From the terrorised visitor there came the most awful shriek of horror as he turned and ran from the premises. His throat was struggling to make coherent sounds as he galloped outside. Vesuvius smiled a victory smile.

"We've done it, Sarge."

"At least the lad came in, eh? Lots wouldn't. That body was heavy. I thought he was going to slip off the brush-head."

"My hand's bloody cold!" Vesuvius stuffed his chilled hand deep into his pocket for warmth.

Congratulating themselves the two conspirators left the mortuary and locked the door. But as they walked away the figure of PC Sean O'Malley was walking boldly towards them.

"Good morning, Sergeant," he said very pleasantly. "I was just coming to check the mortuary."

"Just coming?" smiled Bairstow. "You've not been?"

"No, I got delayed."

"You did?"

"Yes, Sergeant, a minor delay, but a delay none the less."

It was too dark for O'Malley to see the swift glance that passed between his colleagues.

"Anything serious, Sean?" Bairstow used his Christian name quite affably.

"A car without lights, Sergeant."

"Really, where?"

"Just around the corner. The minister of the chapel, in fact. Well, to be honest, his wife. Mrs Sheila Newby. A nice lady."

"You've booked her, at this time of the morning?"

"I'm afraid so, Sergeant. It seems her sister-in-law was very ill, so she and her husband, the Reverend Newby, drove over to Bradford to be with her. They remained until the early hours and drove back, returning home a few minutes ago. I chanced to be in the street and noticed that the rear light on the offside was not working. I decided to interview the driver and make a report. As it happened, the car turned in nearby, to the Manse. I interviewed the driver, who is also the owner of the car that is Mrs Newby, wife of the minister of this chapel. I have reported her for not showing obligatory lights during the hours of darkness."

"You haven't, Sean!"

"Rules are rules, Sergeant."

"So what are you doing now?"

"I have inspected the documents relating to the car and they are all in order. I am now resuming normal patrol, Sergeant, and was on my way to check the mortuary for security."

"You've not been in?"

"No, but the Reverend Newby has."

"Has he?" chorused the plotters. "When?"

"Just now. He flew past me, I'm afraid, on his way home, and wouldn't stop to talk. Perhaps he was very upset at his wife being reported . . ."

"How did *he* come to check the mortuary, Sean?" Bairstow's tone hardened.

"When I was interviewing his wife he suddenly remembered that he had left it open for a body to be taken in, a sudden death of a tramp. He is a key-holder on behalf of the chapel, you see. He thought he would rush around just to check while he was on his feet. As I said, Sergeant, he's been but did not stop to talk to me. One cannot always be popular, can one, if one does one's duty? The poor man. Fancy having a wife who doesn't care enough about her vehicle to see that the lights are correct and in working order."

"The mortuary is locked now," said Sergeant Bairstow softly.

"I'll just check it to be sure, Sergeant. I believe in doing things myself, just to be on the safe side. Shall I see you again?"

"Not tonight," said Sergeant Bairstow. "Tomorrow perhaps, eh, Vesuvius?"

"Yes, Sergeant," smiled Vesuvius, who didn't really like ministers of religion either.

CHAPTER TEN

Oh woman! Lovely woman! Nature made
thee to temper man.
THOMAS OTWAY — *Venice Preserved*

It was Ogden Nash in his declining years who said he preferred
to forget both pairs of glasses and to pass his time saluting
strange women and grandfather clocks. The performance of
night-duty is somewhat similar because the creatures one sees in
the fading light may be precious friends of the opposite sex for
whom a whistle might be appropriate, or they might be ogres in
the form of sergeants, inspectors or even superintendents from
whom constables prefer to conceal themselves.

During that overwhelming tiredness which descends at
the dead of night other shapes can be seen, horrid, ghostly
outlines which are the figments of sheer exhaustion coupled
with an overworked imagination and bad eyesight. It is these
misshapen things that, I am sure, gave rise to tales of medi-
eval monsters, dragons, evil spirits and devils. In a normal
state of health and vision these can be seen to be trees, rocky
outcrops, lampposts, pillar-boxes and even reflections.

Apart from seeing visions, there is little doubt that the
night-hours have a randy effect upon the male person, and

policemen are no exception. The ratio of ordinary males to police males is such that there are many more ordinary males who feel randy at night and who seek to satisfy their lusts in strange places. This is not to say policemen don't satisfy their lusts — it is merely to point out that any night will witness fewer lusty policemen than lusty males of other kinds. The satisfaction of lust can become illegal, but more often than not it is merely embarrassing, sometimes to the participants and sometimes to the beholders.

Patrolling constables often stumble across couples who are actively engaged in a demonstration of mutual affection. This is one of the unforeseen concessions of working night-duty, for if one cannot enjoy those pleasures oneself because of one's devotion to duty, there seems no reason to deny the same pleasures to the people under one's care.

Love therefore continues unabated at night. It happens in bed, in doorways, in cars, in alleys and shop doorways, in cinemas, in seaside shelters, hotel bedrooms, Italian gardens, and even on the top of ornamental rockeries and beside fishponds.

If it happens out of doors, it is fairly certain the policeman will find it and be suitably embarrassed. It is possible that if it happens in bed, the policeman will be involved. If that sentence can be interpreted in more ways than one, what it really means is that love in bed can cause what we term "a breach of the peace", if the man and woman are not married to each other. These rows or disturbances are known as "domestics"; love really has little to do with such traumatic events, although sex has a lot to do with it, and it is not uncommon for a man to leap into bed with a woman who is not his wife, then for the husband to return and make a disturbing discovery. It happens all the time and trouble brews; the police are called, and another domestic problem is wrapped up with a summons and lots of local publicity.

Ingenious and skilful lovers find places where they cannot be caught and where prying eyes cannot see them. In truth there is no such place, but lovers are blind to this simple fact. Off they go in their passion-wagon to carry out their nefarious activities in conditions of total secrecy, while in truth the whole world knows they are at it. Little men with binoculars and dirty raincoats know about them, children know about them, poachers and gamekeepers know about them, other lovers know about them, and you can bet your last penny that the local policeman knows about them. Unlike the rest, he keeps this information to himself because it might become useful ammunition at a later date. Exactly how useful will never be known in advance, but the natural caution of a constable tells him that secrecy is by far the best policy if he catches a local celebrity in furtive turmoil with "another woman". Such information is carefully noted for future reference.

Incidents of this kind so often involve people you would never believe would get into such interesting situations. Policemen learn never to be amazed at anything, but there are times when we are truly surprised.

One of my surprises involved Miss Prudence Proctor. For some months I did not know she existed, but gradually the name cropped up on male lips from time to time, and I began to grow curious about the personality who bore that name. By dint of careful, if oblique questioning, I learned that she lived in Elsinby, occupying a small cottage which nestled behind some trees. It was therefore out of sight from the road through the village, and the approach was along a short, muddy lane. The lovely yellow stone cottage with its red pantile roof squatted among the trees and there was a patch of pleasing rose-garden and lawns before it.

I learned, through more diligent inquiries, that the back of the house excited a good deal more interest than the front, particularly among the male population. This was due to its balcony. It seems that the balcony had been constructed by a previous owner and it led from the French windows of the main bedroom, now excitingly occupied by Miss Prudence Proctor. She lived alone, I discovered, and for many weeks I never set eyes on the lady.

Eventually I noticed her walking proudly down the village street en route to the post office. At the time I did not know that this was *the* Prudence Proctor of whom I had heard so much because she was a very smart middle-aged woman walking erect and confidently towards me. She would be about forty years old, I estimated, with dark hair bound about her head and lashed into a tight bun. Her face was pink and pleasant, and she had a lovely smile. She nodded "good morning" to me as I patrolled along my way. She wore a sober grey two-piece costume, white blouse with a red bow at the throat and a pair of black court shoes. She carried a black handbag and did not wear a hat.

From her appearance I judged she was either a top businessman's secretary or a schoolteacher, or maybe someone in the professions like a doctor, dentist or barrister. I was to learn subsequently that she had no known occupation and appeared to live on private means, although she did occasional work with the BBC on audience surveys and similar statistical experiments. She was not married and, I understand, never had been. She lived alone in that delightful cottage and kept two ginger cats. She was quiet, law-abiding, attractive, and articulate — the sort of woman any man would be pleased to know, on both a professional and personal level.

At our first meeting, she stopped me to ask advice. She had a nephew, she said, who was shortly leaving school and he had expressed an interest in the police service as a career. He wanted to join as a cadet and hoped to become a full-time member of the regular force.

After outlining the necessary qualifications I offered to obtain some leaflets and brochures for the lady and asked her name. Then it was that I learned she was the famous Miss Prudence Proctor of Acorn Cottage, Elsinby.

Her physical appearance made me unsure whether I was talking to the person whose antics set the village men aflame with passion from time to time. But if local information and gossip was accurate, then this indeed was the lady. After noting her name and address and promising faithfully I would secure the necessary information, I bade her "good morning" and off she went, walking proudly about her business.

I found it very, very difficult to accept that this was the woman whose name was always on the male lips of Elsinby.

There must be some mistake; they must be wrong. This was a straight, serious even dowdy woman, and I began to wonder if the men were involving me in some weird and obtuse type of Yorkshire joke.

A week later I received the necessary literature from our Recruiting Department and decided to call at Acorn Cottage to deliver it. I undertook this duty during an evening patrol and it would be around seven o'clock when I called. Prudence answered my knock dressed in a long, close-fitting woollen dress. Over a cup of tea she told me that she had knitted it herself. She provided me with biscuits, and I answered all her questions about a policeman's life. In all, I spent about an hour in her company and found her very intelligent and interesting.

I saw no more of her for several weeks. Because of what I had heard, I must confess I did not seek her out, nor did I venture to call upon her to find out how her nephew had progressed with his application. The next time she crossed my line of duty was one night in early August. The air was balmy and mild with the scent of honeysuckle and roses, and all about Elsinby the cornfields were a glow of yellow. The summer fruit was ripening — blackberries, apples, pears, plums and wild berries abounded, and the late summer was ideal. It was a lovely time to live in a rural community.

I was on night-duty and had decided to drive the little Ford around my own patch to check some of the pubs. Day-trippers and visitors were in the district and some tended to abuse the hospitality of the landlords by staying late. This created antagonism among the local drinkers because it was their privilege to drink after hours, being friends of the licensees. Such privileges must not be abused.

For this reason I liked to pop into my local pubs just before closing-time to eject everyone, and the appearance of the uniform was generally sufficient to do the trick. At 11.10, therefore, I popped into the Hopbind Inn at Elsinby, which was heaving with warm bodies and thick with heavy smoke.

"Time, gentlemen, please," called George when he espied me, and the usual deathly hush descended. Gradually everyone drank up and left, one by one, the visitors being the first to remove themselves, and the local folks hanging back as they always did. During the exodus, one of them sidled up to me and whispered, "Full moon tonight, Mr Rhea."

This was Isaac Samuels, a local poacher.

"Is it?" I asked, wondering why this should be of interest to me.

"Aye, midnight or thereabouts. Full moon." He could see I was not comprehending the hidden significance of this occurrence. "You know!" he said, pointing vaguely to a locality behind the pub, somewhere out in the woods.

I scratched my head. "Sorry, Zaccy," I had to admit defeat. "I'm not with you."

"Full moon," he repeated in a stage whisper. "You'll be there, eh?"

I must have looked decidedly stupid because he led me outside and said, "Acorn Cottage — we're all going up there, now."

"Why?" I asked in total innocence.

"Thoo knows," he said, his old head nodding in its own secret language. "Full moon . . ." and he nudged my arm, grinning all the while through his assorted black teeth.

"Can I come?" I had to ask, wondering if their full moon sojourn was legal.

"Aye, course you can. We all are."

"Show me," I was interested and still did not link this with Prudence.

He led me stealthily out of the back door of the Hopbind Inn and along a stony lane with a row of cottages and a school at one side. We turned left at a junction in the lane and I found myself tramping across leaf mould and grass as he took me by the light of the moon through a woodland glade.

The path was clearly defined by the passage of many feet and we climbed through picturesque wooded areas in almost total silence. As a poacher he could negotiate woodland more silently than a ghost, and I was equally accustomed to being silent, although I couldn't compete with him in these surroundings. We made our way steeply into the wood until we veered left and returned towards the village, albeit at a higher level.

Within five minutes we were in a wooded glade, deep among the trees, and I was surprised to find about twenty men there, all totally silent. Some turned and smiled as I made my way into the arena. I now realised we were directly behind the home of Miss Prudence Proctor. It was now that I saw the famous balcony, showing clearly in the night due to its coat of brilliant white paint. The cottage was in darkness.

"What's going on?" I whispered to Isaac.

"Thoo'll see," was all he said, nudging me and laughing softly. "Thoo'll see, Mr Rhea."

It was clear that no further enlightenment was to be given, so I waited for about twenty minutes, wondering if Sergeant Blaketon was looking for me. I daren't leave now for I was sure all was going to be revealed. Several more gentlemen arrived to make a considerable audience in the wood, every one of them standing silently behind Acorn Cottage.

Then things began to happen. The French windows of the bedroom were opened on to the balcony and I could just distinguish two long smooth arms pushing them open. The bedroom inside was in darkness, and then lights came on. These were not the normal household lights, but were in brilliant and exotic colours — red, green, purple and many others, all combining to give a low, vibrant hue to the room. Pulsating music then began to sound from that room; it was a tune I did not recognise, but it had a hint of gypsy magic as it came from the record-player, amplified so that we could hear it clearly. Finally, Prudence appeared.

Silhouetted against the colourful background and sensuously bathed in alternating colours was a tall woman in swirling drapes of some lightweight fabric, silk, maybe, or satin or even something more flimsy. To the stirring intensity of that music she began to dance on the balcony. Her hair, long and dark, swirled as she moved, and her eyes flashed in the changing light.

The long-playing record provided a selection of vibrant music which grew faster and faster and more furious as we watched. The lights changed all the time, sometimes very low and dim, exchanging suddenly to bright and piercing rays as they focused on the entrancing woman who danced before our eyes. Faster and faster went the music, faster and faster went Miss Prudence Proctor until the thin veils began to disappear. With the skill of a professional strip-tease artiste, she began to remove her veils, one by one, gracefully and sensually, all the time maintaining perfect time to the changing mood of the music.

I looked at the men. They were transfixed. Their eyes were glued on the unbelievable scene before them, and I smiled. They'd have to pay pounds for this sort of entertainment in the city, yet here she was, free and totally uninhibited, providing an exotic evening for her audience in a Yorkshire wood. As the music intensified, so did she. As the first record finished, the second dropped into place to continue the rhythm as more veils were discarded. It was clear that every single one was going to be removed tonight.

And they were. One by one she removed her seven gossamer veils in movements that spoke of total devotion to her art. She was aided by a lovely body against a backcloth of moving light and throbbing music. In that sylvan setting, her rustic audience made not a sound. There were no whistles, applause or shouts — nothing. It was as if they knew that any sound from them would stop the show, perhaps forever. It would be like waking up before the end of a wonderful dream.

But the display did end. The final veil was discarded in a smooth and beautiful movement to reveal the mature splendour of this strange and compelling woman. At that point the music stopped, and the lights went out. She vanished as suddenly as she had appeared.

Silently the awestruck men returned home through the wood, not speaking and not making a sound. They would tell their wives they'd been talking late at the pub, and no one would be any wiser.

"Does she know you lads watch her?" I asked Isaac when we neared the village.

"Nay, lad," he laughed. "She's no idea."

Personally I doubted this, but did not press the matter.

"How did you know she'd do that?" I asked him.

"It's full moon," he answered. "She does it at every full moon."

He made that statement as if it explained everything. Perhaps it did.

If frustrated ladies wish to prance around naked at full moon in the privacy of their own homes, it is barely a police problem. On the other hand, there are many ladies who are not frustrated and who relieve their pent-up emotions by love-making in all sorts of unlikely places. While this is likewise not a police problem per se, it is true that many a night-duty constable has helped cars out of rivers and bogs in which they have inexplicably found themselves while their occupants were busy with other things. Similarly, many a policeman has stumbled across couples busy in public places like carparks, pub forecourts, and even in the street. I was once told of a naked pair hard at it in the back seat of their Ford Consul in full view of the incoming customers at a local pub. They seemed totally unabashed by the interesting display they were providing, and, although none of the drinkers complained, the landlord did ring me about it. He didn't want the reputation of his pub tarnished by powerful rumours of open-air orgies.

I proceeded to the scene, as we say in official jargon, and sure enough the story was accurate. A naked man and woman were very actively making love in the car, apparently oblivious to the fact that their performance was in a very open and public carpark. Acting in the best interests of the general public, I tapped on the window. After the passage of a moment or two, it was wound down by a man looking very flushed about the face and perspiring somewhat from his recent exertions.

"What's up, mate?" he asked, wiping his brow.

"You realise where you are?" I put to him, wondering how to open this conversation.

"Aye," he said.

"Well, you're causing embarrassment," I continued. "The folks in the pub are embarrassed."

"Not them!" he wiped his brow again. "They'll be lapping it up. Look, it's not illegal, is it?"

"It depends where you do it and who you do it with."

"She's the missus."

"Whose missus?" I asked the obvious question.

"Mine," he said flatly. "She's my missus."

"Well, can't you go home?"

"Home?" he growled, peering up at me. "I have no home. We live with her parents, the bloody-in-laws. Her mother's an interfering old cuss and we haven't a minute to ourselves. Paper-thin walls, an' all. No privacy even in bed. We can't relax, there's no fun. So we go out and do it in the car."

"But not on a pub forecourt?"

"Couldn't wait," he said. "Look mate, I'm sorry if I caused upset, honest. I thought the windows were steamed up."

"They are," I agreed, "but the light from the pub shines right in, and although you couldn't be seen in detail, there's no mistaking what was happening."

"There's no peace, luv," he said to his wife. "Come on, let's go."

"There's a disused aerodrome a mile up the road," I advised him. "First turn left."

"Is there?"

"Let's go there," said a sweet voice from the depths of the car, and they did. I checked that his car number was correct and tallied with his name. The woman really was his wife. I felt a twinge of sorrow for people who live in conditions so appalling that they must carry out this most private of acts in a public place. Privacy is a valuable commodity.

There are many furtive lovers who perform in public places which they believe to be private, and they do so because they do not wish to be caught by their respective husbands/ wives/ boyfriends/ girlfriends/ lovers. In truth, illicit romance of this kind is usually discovered, and a tryst of this sort captured our imagination late one Friday night.

We are fortunate in North Yorkshire to have lots of open countryside and spacious moorland areas which are ideal for those who wish to "get away from it all", even for an hour or two. Many of the moorland heights and green valleys have become rendezvous points for lovers of all ages and both sexes, and if one travels around at night, like policemen do, one sees cars, vans, tents and uncovered people dotted about like daisies on a lawn. The period of peak activity is around eleven o'clock in the evening which broadly coincides with pub closing-times. Some of the very hardy and determined remain there until one or even two o'clock. On a winter's night, this demands devotion of an extraordinary kind.

Such a couple were John Withy and Sheila Grove. John was about thirty-three years old, married with two children, and a painter and decorator by trade. He was a busy man who successfully ran his own business, and, although he worked long hours, he did have a certain amount of freedom of movement. This was usefully employed among the many desirable ladies he met in the course of his work, lots of whom wanted their fronts decorating. As a consequence, John had many romances, most of which were short-lived in the extreme, even as short as half-an-hour, but once in a while he would find someone with whom he fell deeply in love.

Such a woman was Mrs Sheila Grove. She was a delightfully vague sort of girl whose husband was a commercial traveller. He was away from home for lengthy periods and Sheila grew somewhat lonesome. John had been contracted to paint the Grove household, and, as a consequence, Sheila invited him in for a cup of tea. From that stage the romance blossomed. Sheila, however, was a crafty lover and, upon realising what the neighbours might think, took great pains to conceal her new-found friendship. She let the kettle steam up the kitchen windows or met John away from the family home.

Romances of this kind never escape the notice of neighbours. Neighbours see all, hear all and say everything; what they don't see, they invent, and what they can't invent isn't worth thinking about. Word therefore got around to everyone except John's wife that he was very busy decorating Mrs Grove's panels and architraves. John, meanwhile, had informed his wife that he was working late on an important and rushed job, which to a certain extent was true.

Much of his overtime and rushing was spent in his little van high on the North Yorkshire moors on the edge of Aidensfield beat. His favourite pitch was a lofty spot on a moorland ridge beneath some pine-trees. A small knot of pines grew from this exposed ridge and they were bent due to the prevailing winds never dying away, but this slender row of timber provided some sort of shelter for his little van, marked "Withy — Decorator". It would proceed to that lovely place once or twice a week and inside its cosy interior John and Sheila would commence their stripping and pasting.

During my routine patrols, I passed the van several times but did not disturb the happy couple. It was a very lonely area and they caused no harm to anyone. I did not investigate because I knew who it was and what they were doing, and it was no part of a policeman's duty to interfere with moral misbehaviour of a personal kind. I did wonder, however, when and how their little game would be discovered. Invariably, such liaisons are discovered, and I felt sure John and Sheila were no exception.

It was very appropriate that their meeting place was known as Lovers Leap, for legend said that years ago towards the turn of the century a young couple leapt to their deaths from this point. This was due to some parental opposition to their romance.

Sometimes on my day off I would walk here with Mary and the children for the vantage point provided a wonderful view of the surrounding countryside. It was breathtakingly beautiful. From the small plateau beneath the stooping firs the ground fell steeply away across a heathery and bracken-covered hillside. That hillside is covered with young silver-birch trees, knotted briars and acres of tightly growing bracken as it slopes steeply into a ravine many feet below.

The ravine contains a moorland stream of purest water which bubbles happily over granite as it makes its way, full of minerals, to the sea. Beyond is the wild, colourful expanse of the North Yorkshire moors with Fylingdales Early Warning Station in the background and, beyond that, the romance of the wild North Sea.

At night the view is equally grand because the valleys and hillsides are dotted with tiny lights, shining like glow-worms, and the dark block of moorland suggests intrigue, danger, mystery, and of course, romance, just like the inside of Withy's decorating van.

It was to this location therefore that John Withy and his van, with Sheila at his side, proceeded one night, intent upon a spot of dressing down and undercoating. I was on duty at the time, patrolling in the little Ford Anglia, and had no occasion to visit Lovers Leap that night — not initially, that is. From what I learned later it seems that the happy pair, excited and keen, had reached the site of their future passion. In the cosiness of the decorating van, with its load of paint, wallpaper, ladders and associated tins and bottles of fluid they had commenced their evening ritual.

Kisses and cuddles developed into slaps and tickles, and in no time all their clothing was thrown off as they settled down to the real business of the evening. The two warm and naked bodies writhed and pumped in sheer ecstasy, although they were rather hampered because they had to manipulate themselves into all kinds of positions on the front seats.

Unfortunately, the rear of the van was laden with tomorrow's wallpapers, paint and brush, cleaning fluid, and there was no room for humans in love. This did not deter John and Sheila — in fact, it spurred them to make a decent job on a poor location, and soon the little van was bouncing rhythmically to the movements of the blissful pair.

Their frantic and ecstatic writhing performed a small act which was destined to lead to their eternal embarrassment. Their movements knocked the handbrake of the little van and it released its grip on the vehicle. Slowly but surely the handbrake abandoned its post under the undulating movements of the couple, and the vehicle began to move, very slowly at first.

In their climaxing moments, the couple did not notice this gentle motion, and before long the van was running down the slope. Very slowly it moved from its parking place while every delirious action of the pair inside gave the van more momentum. Soon it was travelling quite fast, and before John and Sheila realised what was happening, the van was careering out of control down the steep, bracken-covered slope of Lovers Leap.

It was too late to stop it. Panic-stricken, John leapt from the object of his passion and managed to open his door, shouting for his lover to jump. Both jumped out. There was nothing else they could do. They rolled over and over in the thick bracken, Sheila screaming with fear, pain and shock as the bouncing van careered along its downward route, rattling and crashing through the thick undergrowth and demolishing a host of tiny silver birches. It could go no farther than the gully.

As expected, there was an almighty crash as the van and its contents dropped like a stone into the ravine and burst into flames. Petrol, paint and the paraphernalia of decorating, all combined to create a time-bomb within the van. An enormous explosion followed as the entire thing blew up. Fires broke out along the hillside as the dry bracken began to burn and soon the intense flames of the blazing van roared into the heavens, illuminating the night sky for miles around.

The couple whose hot passion had literally set the countryside alight stood naked on the hillside, clutching one another and bleeding from numerous scratches and cuts. Sheila was crying softly into John's arms as he simply stood there, spotlighted in the dancing flames and not daring to believe this had really happened.

The noise and brilliance of the display attracted the attention of many eyes, and in no time the police station and Fire Brigade offices were notified. Emergency fire tenders roared to the scene, and I was contacted at a telephone kiosk only minutes later. The constable at the desk at Malton gabbled something about an aircraft crash, and immediately I was roaring to the location. There was no difficulty tracing the scene, for once I gained the elevation of the hills I was guided easily by the flames and smoke. I was first to arrive, and I parked among those bending pines wondering what had caused this turmoil. The entire hillside was ablaze, crackling and roaring in the eternal wind.

And there, shining in the light of the fire, I saw two naked figures struggling up the hillside towards me. The man was clutching a weeping woman as they struggled, bleeding and battered, towards my car. And they wore not a stitch of clothing between them. There were all kinds of jokes I could have made at that point, but while it was undoubtedly the place for a joke, it was certainly not the time. I called to them and suggested they get into the police car. Inside there was my cape and an overcoat, and I advised them to use those while I decided what to do about the blazing moor.

I ventured part of the way down the hillside and got as far as a small area of burning bracken, which happily had been contained by a patch of sphagnum moss. From there I could see the van deep in the gully, still burning fiercely and emitting sparks and fumes in its death throes. It was beyond any help. As I climbed back up the steep incline, the Fire Brigade arrived, and I was able to inform the leading fireman of the situation.

My chief concern was that the whole moor would catch fire, a regular event on these hills, but it seemed the fortunate location of the sphagnum moss had largely eliminated that likelihood. Members of the brigade ventured down the slope and finally began to spray the burning wreck with foam, smothering the blaze and quenching the flames. Others tackled small pockets of fire among the vegetation, and the moor was given a liberal soaking of water. This soaking continued, using water from the gully, just in case the fire did penetrate the upper layer of moorland topsoil. But within a couple of hours the fire was out, and the brigade left the scene. It hadn't been as bad as we had feared.

Back at my car, I found Sheila shivering in my cape and John wrapped in my overcoat. She had dried her eyes but was in a state of shock as he sat dumbfounded with his arm about her.

"So what happened?" I asked.

He told me his story.

"You've got some explaining to do," I added when he had finished.

"What can I tell the wife?" he pleaded. "What shall I do?"

"I'm not going to put ideas into your head, John," I said. "But first you need clothing."

"My husband has some old clothes," Sheila offered. "I can tell him I threw them out."

"How can I explain to my wife?" John pleaded. "What will she think if I turn up in different clothes?"

"I'm sure you'll think of something," I returned to the driving seat and started the engine. "Well, who's first?"

"My house," Sheila said.

"What about hospital for a check-up?" I suggested.

"Not likely, there's enough explaining to do," John said. "We're all right, apart from cuts and bruises."

"Take us to my house," Sheila repeated. "Your overalls are still there, aren't they, John?"

"So they are," he smiled. "Yes, do that. I'll manage somehow."

I took them to Sheila's home and went inside with them, each as naked as a babe. They were not shy in my presence and when both were dressed, Sheila in a sweater and slacks and John in his overalls, I had a coffee with them.

I left feeling it had been an interesting night. Days later I could not confirm a rumour that John's van had been stolen while he was on the job, although the rumour circulated the village for weeks. I have no idea how John explained to his wife about his missing clothes, but I can confirm they were not reported lost or stolen.

If love and its side effects cause problems to people beyond the police service, they also create problems within. Policemen are like other lusty male humans who, from time to time, succumb to the charms of lovely ladies who are not their wives or sweethearts. Many have risked their careers for a few moments of tender illicit love.

It is refreshing, therefore, to discover a policeman who loves his wife so much that he risks his career to spend blissful moments in her company.

Such a man was Constable Simon Simpkins, a tall, slender, twenty-two-year-old with a penchant for quizzing scooter-riders and an intense dislike of children who sucked ice-lollies. His arrival at Eltering coincided with the arrival of Inspector Bert Minskip at the nearby Sub-Divisional Headquarters. Both these arrivals coincided with my posting to Aidensfield and we met from time to time.

Inspector Minskip, it had been rumoured, was with us only temporarily having been sent from one of the busy urban areas of the county where the pace and quality of life had been too much for his sensitive nature. Headquarters had considered it wise to post him briefly to a rural patch where life was pleasant and straightforward, where the people were human and where he could exercise a different sort of policeman-ship. His posting was a kind of official holiday, a period of adjustment and unwinding for him, a spell without pressures and lacking the problems of an inspector in a busy urban station.

The snag was that Inspector Minskip found the solitude and lack of sordid criminal happenings rather boring and he occupied his time in the close supervision of his men. This was disconcerting for rural bobbies who traditionally enjoyed a great sense of freedom. The outcome was that instead of relaxing and enjoying his three months with us Inspector Minskip became very neurotic about the affairs of the station, the timings, personal lives and duties of those officers under his command. He was perhaps unfortunate that PC Simpkins, newly married and fascinated with his new life, was one of the officers beneath his care.

I met PC Simpkins once or twice and found him a very pleasant young fellow, if a little immature at times. Sometimes we shared night-shifts; from time to time when I was patrolling from Aidensfield he would be on duty in the southern area of our division and we would meet at Eltering Police Station for a chat over our supper. He was keen to learn the job and was particularly anxious to understand the intricacies of traffic legislation as he had ambitions to become a Road Traffic patrol car driver.

It was this ambition which appeared to upset Inspector Minskip. He believed that all good policemen patrolled on foot or on cycles and that traffic men were not really police officers but merely glorified forms of taxi drivers. He therefore allocated to young Simpkins many tours of cycle duty, hoping to impress the lad that a constable aboard a pedal cycle can hear and see many things of value to a patrolling policeman.

One night in late summer I was patrolling around Eltering town when I saw young Simpkins on a pedal cycle. It would be around one o'clock in the morning and I stopped to speak to him.

"Morning Simon," I said, stepping out of the little Ford. "Are you lost? You're a bit off your patch, aren't you?"

He smiled dreamingly. "Yes, I am, but I know you'll keep it to yourself. I'm going to have a quick visit to my wife. She gets lonely when I'm on nights."

"Ah!" I understood the situation very well.

"I thought I'd manage an hour with her. I reckon this bike'll get me there and back without being missed."

"Isn't Inspector Minskip around?" I asked.

"No, he saw me at eleven and said he was going home to bed. There's no sergeants on duty either."

"Best of British!" I wished him and off he went, looking gladsome and elated.

He pedalled into the darkness with the official red light wavering slightly as he tried to coax extra speed from the cumbersome machine. I watched him turn a corner to pedal his way to his love-nest. He would have to report at Eltering at six o'clock to book off duty, so that gave him plenty of time to achieve his purpose, and he would have to risk the consequences of missing one or two points.

It was with considerable surprise that I found Inspector Minskip waiting for me at my four o'clock point at Whemmelby Kiosk. Like young Simon I thought he'd gone to bed. Clearly that had been a tale to lull the men into a false sense of security, and he had taken the decision to drive into the wilds to check that I wasn't sleeping on the job. I wondered about Simon . . .

Inspector Minskip asked if everything was correct and I issued suitable noises to assure him that I had the entire Sub-Division under my firm control and that no villains were abroad.

"Have you seen young Simpkins?" he asked after the formal business was over.

"No, sir," I said firmly.

"I've searched all likely places for him," said the inspector. "I'll bet the young bugger's sneaked off home to see his missus. He can't keep off her . . . he'll wear himself out. You know what these newlyweds are."

And off he went.

It was clear to me that he'd suspected the love-sick constable of sneaking home during duty-time and had hatched this little plot to catch him. That meant trouble for young Simon and I wondered what Minskip would do next.

Unfortunately, I had to return to my own area and was not able to witness the end of this story although the finale did reach me in a roundabout way, as stories are prone to do in police circles.

It seems that a highly satisfied Constable Simpkins left his love-nest on the official cycle to wind his contented way back to Eltering Police Station. There he would report off duty and go home again, lucky chap. The cycle was going well, the morning was fine and dry; he was completely happy and very much in love with his beautiful wife. In spite of his euphoric state he was very alert, and I am given to understand that it was with considerable surprise that he noticed the bulky figure of Inspector Minskip standing beneath a streetlamp. He was positioned near a roundabout on the approaches to the town.

Constable Simpkins knew the game was up, but he had almost quarter of a mile to consider his next action and dream up his excuses. There was no other road which could be used as an escape route. Minskip had obviously observed his approach for he had stepped from beneath the streetlight and now stood in the middle of the road awaiting the cornered youngster. As he cycled those final, nerve-racking yards, Simpkins could see his career evaporating. There'd be no motor patrol, he would be disciplined and kicked out of the service with a black mark for ever against his name. All this crossed his mind as he cycled closer to the waiting inspector.

How much of the story which follows is the untarnished truth and how much is the result of subsequent retelling by fascinated *raconteurs* will never be known, but an account of the finale to this drama circulated our Sub-Division like this: It seems that the waiting inspector called upon PC Simpkins and his bicycle to stop and explain their presence at this place.

Simpkins, however, had totally ignored that order and had cycled a few yards past the inspector where he had dismounted and leaned the cycle against a streetlight. Without a word to the puzzled inspector, PC Simpkins had swiftly climbed up the lamppost to sit astride the crossbar at the top. There he had clung to the lamp standard rather as a monkey would do. And there he sat, never speaking a word to the bewildered inspector below.

We were assured that Inspector Minskip had stamped, ranted and raved at the base of the lamppost, shouting orders for the constable to descend and threatening all kinds of dire circumstances when he did. The outcome was that PC Simpkins simply remained where he was. He had said not one word and had merely gazed heavenwards into a sky brightening with the light of a new day. As Minskip had circled the base, sometimes threatening, sometimes pleading, PC Simpkins had never moved one inch, nor had he spoken one word. It had been as if he were never there.

We are given to understand that this performance lasted some twenty minutes after which Inspector Minskip announced he was going back to the office to report the matter to the Superintendent by telephone. He would arrange for a sharp disciplinary lesson for young Simpkins.

Inspector Minskip had then walked away, huffing and puffing his indignation and anger, and had undertaken the long walk back to the police office on foot. Having been such a keen advocate of foot patrols he could scarcely have used a car.

Once the inspector was out of sight, PC Simpkins had descended and rapidly boarded his trusty cycle. He raced back to the office, beating the panting inspector by a good fifteen minutes. He had had sufficient time to ring the duty inspector at Malton to express his concern about the mental attitude of Inspector Minskip.

"What's up, Simpkins?" the duty inspector had asked, noting the hint of positive alarm in Simpkins' voice.

"Well, sir, it's difficult, but Mr Minskip has just accused me of sitting up a lamppost two miles off my beat. He didn't seem able to understand what I was trying to tell him, you see, and I was very worried, so I came straight here and rang you. I thought the Superintendent ought to know about it . . ."

And so, after a lengthy conversation with PC Simpkins, the inspector at Malton had telephoned the Superintendent at Divisional Headquarters. The matter had been sufficiently important to drag the great man from his bed, and he listened carefully to the constable's unlikely story.

There had been recent concern about the mental condition of Inspector Minskip; the constable's story sounded so unusual, so outlandish . . . The following day, lengthy interviews were arranged with him and he vowed he had never been off his beat and had certainly never shinned up a lamppost.

The outcome of all this was that poor old Inspector Minskip was advised, in a manner he could not refuse, to attend the Police Convalescent Home for three months' complete rest.

We understand he found it beneficial.

THE END

ALSO BY NICHOLAS RHEA

Don't miss a book in the series — join our mailing list:

www.joffebooks.com

Thank you for reading this book. If you enjoyed it please leave feedback on Amazon or Goodreads, and if there is anything we missed or you have a question about, then please get in touch. The author and publishing team appreciate your feedback and time reading this book.

We're very grateful to eagle-eyed readers who take the time to contact us. Please send any errors you find to corrections@joffebooks.com

Made in the USA
Middletown, DE
31 January 2023

23627616R00120